the 70s

Welcome to the 1970s Book of Days, <u>the</u> place to keep all your important dates.

Use it to jot down birthdays, anniversaries and other notable events about family and friends that you don't want to forget. Plus there's an address book in back too.

Every page is brimming with a '70s pop culture potpourri of television, music, movies, fashion, theater, bestsellers and more, like:

America rediscovers its roots (January)... **A heavyweight fight inspires an Oscar-winning movie franchise** (March)... **Anti-war rallies rock the nation** (May)... **Reggae crowns its first superstar** (July)... **A chocolate chip empire is born** (August)... **Punk's high priestess ignites a fashion craze** (November)... and on and on.

So enjoy these tidbits and tales, milestones and miscellanea, gathered together in one place for the first time ever: the 1970s Book of Days.

And check out the other Books of Days, trivia contests and more at **www.365edge.com.**

Hunter S. Thompson

Andy Warhol and the Velvet Underground

GET THE 365 EDGE

TELL TALE
PRESS

The 1970s Book of Days

Writer: Harvey Solomon
Designers: Ken Camner, Ross Waldorf
Contributors: Richard Appel, Fang Huang, Jane Kondon, Alice Morton, Barbara Osborn, William Solomon, Scott Tambert, Steve Taravella

Special thanks to the staff at the Library of Congress for providing generous assistance and expertise

Cover and page one images: iStockphoto, Library of Congress New York World-Telegram & Sun Collection, U.S. National Archives, Ueli Frey, Michael Reeve, Markadet

Printed in China

ISBN-13: 978-0-9760485-3-4

January

1 A Spring Preview issue of Gloria Steinem's *Ms.* magazine sells 300,000 copies in eight days, paving the way for its monthly debut in July (1972)

2 Conservation becomes the new norm as President Nixon signs a bill mandating a maximum national highway speed of 55 m.p.h. (1974)

3 With John Lennon on holiday, the other three Beatles gather at Abbey Road Studios to record Harrison's *I, Me Mine* for their last album, *Let It Be* (1970)

4 Broadway producers shift curtain time from the traditional 8:30 p.m. to seven, and by season's end see a 17% increase in ticket sales (1971)

5 *All My Children* begins its long run (1970); in two years Mary Fickett wins the first Emmy for a daytime performance as an antiwar mother of a soldier MIA

6 The sophisticated, multi-layered British import *Upstairs, Downstairs*, destined to be PBS's most successful miniseries, debuts (1974)

7 Neighbors of Max Yasgur, on whose property Woodstock was held, sue for $35,000 in property damage (1970)

Library of Congress: N.Y. World-Telegram & Sun Collection

JANUARY 2, 1971
Cigarettes Ciao

In TV's early years many advertisers sponsored programs, and cigarette brands enjoyed a huge presence on the small screen. To offset increasing tobacco ads in the '60s, the FCC required stations to run one anti-smoking PSA for every three cigarette ads. In 1969 Congress proposed a ban on all radio and TV cigarette spots. Initially opposed, the tobacco giants realized it was only a matter of time and decided to cooperate. The ban took effect one day after New Years Day, allowing Big Tobacco one final chance to advertise on the popular college bowl football games.

"Winston tastes good like a cigarette should."

—ONE OF THE FIRST CIGARETTE TV ADS

C.B.S.

JANUARY 12, 1971
Make Room For Archie

The stereotypical sitcom of wholesome, homogenized families undergoes a shattering shift with Norman Lear's *All in the Family*. Bigoted arch-conservative patriarch Archie Bunker (Carroll O'Connor) mixes it up with just about everyone from his long-haired, liberal "meathead" son-in-law (Rob Reiner) to his dim but sweet "dingbat" wife (Jean Stapleton). A lightning rod, the show takes a couple months to catch on but goes on to become TV's #1 show for five straight years, spinning off future successes like *Maude* and *The Jeffersons*.

"Boy, the way Glenn Miller played, songs that made the hit parade, guys like us we had it made, those were the days..."

—THEME SONG FROM
ALL IN THE FAMILY

8 The National Book Critics Circle gives its inaugural award for fiction to E.L. Doctorow's *Ragtime* (1976); thirty years later he'll repeat for *The March*

9 In a 3-hour conference call with reporters, reclusive billionaire Howard Hughes exposes Clifford Irving's purported autobiography as a fraud (1972)

10 PBS's *Masterpiece Theatre* debuts with the bawdy *The First Churchills*, but unsure of the show's future host Alistair Cooke has signed only a 1-year contract (1971)

11 Now batting: the American League announces that this season it will experiment with the designated hitter (1973)

12 Mike Nichols' sexually charged *Carnal Knowledge* triggers the arrest, conviction (and eventual overturn) of obscenity charges against a Georgia theater owner (1973)

13 Boston Opera cofounder Sarah Caldwell becomes the first woman to conduct (Verdi's *La Traviata*) at the Metropolitan Opera House (1976)

14 Redd Foxx tones down his raunchy nightclub persona to play a crotchety junk dealer in Norman Lear's *Sanford and Son* (1972)

15 Are they here again? Did they ever leave? *Happy Days* debuts on ABC with budding stars Henry Winkler and Ron Howard (1974)

16 Clean cut song and dance: *Donny and Marie* bows on ABC, with Marie looking especially sharp in her Bob Mackie (Cher's ex-designer) outfits (1976)

17 Oh say can you see... what's going on? Marvin Gaye sings the National Anthem at Super Bowl V (1971)

18 Miami passes a gay rights ordinance, and Anita Bryant immediately mobilizes to have it overturned (1977)

19 A taped phone interview with Bob Dylan by self-styled "Dylanologist" A.J. Weberman, who pores through Dylan's trash, turns nasty and is later released briefly on Folkways Records (1971)

20 Savvy programmer Fred Silverman, who'd steered ABC to #1 with hits like *Charlie's Angels* and *Three's Company,* departs for NBC where his magic touch evaporates (1978)

21 When the Bee Gees' *Saturday Night Fever,* the top selling soundtrack of all time, is ignored by the Oscars a movie spokesman suggests the Academy consists of "retired violinists who probably still play 78s on their Victrolas" (1978)

P.B.S

JANUARY 18, 1973
Real Loud Relations

Years before·the term "reality television" came into vogue came the pioneering Loud family of Santa Barbara, CA. They agreed to put their daily lives under the microscope, or more accurately to be captured on camera for a groundbreaking 12-hour PBS documentary, *An American Family.* America watched entranced as its messy real-life drama enfolded: squabbles, spats, husband Bill's philandering that triggered a divorce and, on this day, wife Pat's NYC trip to visit eldest son Lance, the first openly gay person ever on American television. Controversial and complex, it remains an unequaled watershed television event.

"As new and as significant as the invention of drama or the novel — a new way in which people can learn to look at life."

—ANTHROPOLOGIST MARGARET MEAD ON TELEVISION VERITÉ

JANUARY 23, 1977
Generational Saga

Unsure of its potential, ABC schedules the expensive 12-hour miniseries *Roots* over eight consecutive nights, figuring that if it's a flop at least it will be over soon. Instead, Alex Haley's complex, compelling slave drama captivates America and becomes the most-watched show in TV history. Featuring a rich, ethnically diverse ensemble cast and a star-making turn by young LeVar Burton as Kunta Kinte, *Roots*-mania envelops the country. Based on a Pulitzer prize-winning novel, it goes on to win nine Emmys and a Peabody award. Half the country's population, 100 million people, tune in to the finale on January 30.

"The production and performances are strong... It was a bit disconcerting to cut from the anguished screams of a mother whose oldest son had been enslaved to a blurb for Ben-Gay, for use 'when pain is at its worst.'"

— VARIETY

22 HBO debuts its first championship bout, live from Kingston, Jamaica, mon, as George Foreman TKOs Joe Frazier in round two (1973)

23 Police antics ensue as *Barney Miller* opens a 7-year run on ABC, finally winning the Emmy for outstanding comedy series after its cancellation (1978)

24 Inventor Robert Moog introduces a $2,000 portable Mini-Moog synthesizer, ideal for concert use (1970)

25 After a successful run at a local NYC club, the Woodstock (dubbed Woodchuck) parody *National Lampoon's Lemmings* debuts off Broadway (1973)

26 The sweet soul sounds of the Emotions, embodied in *I Don't Want to Lose Your Love,* turns their album, *Flowers,* gold (500,000 units) (1977)

27 Undefeated? No, Raymond Burr actually lost one case as legal legend *Perry Mason* concludes after a record-breaking 17 seasons (1974)

28 During a White House concert by the Ray Conniff Singers, substitute singer Carol Feraci unfolds a sign ("Stop the Killing") and denounces Nixon's Vietnam War policy (1972)

29 A red, white and blue *Life* magazine cover highlights life on the road with an American institution, Bob Hope (1971)

30 We never, evah do anything nice and easy: Ike and Tina Turner release their raucous, rip-roaring cover of *Proud Mary* (1971)

31 Disney sues the producers of a porno film, *The Happy Hooker,* to force them to remove the Mickey Mouse theme from an orgy scene (1975)

NOTES

JANUARY 31, 1976
Catchy & Kitschy

Adored by the masses and scorned by the critics, ABBA rides their rhythmic, harmonizing act into the stratosphere. Today *Mamma Mia* deposes the 9-week reign of Queen's *Bohemian Rhapsody* atop the UK singles charts, and the onslaught is on. The Swedish quartet, twin husbands and wives, becomes the biggest international pop act of the decade with oodles of hypnotic hits like *Waterloo, SOS, Fernando, Take A Chance On Me* and *Dancing Queen.* In short succession come sold-out tours, a command royal performance, a movie and a *Guinness Book of World Records* mention. With that kind of success, who needs (or heeds) the critics?

"We don't want to write political songs. We don't want to turn our records into speeches."

— BENNY ANDERSSON,
ABBA CO-FOUNDER

February

1 ABC's blockbuster 12-hour *Rich Man, Poor Man,* adapted from Irwin Shaw's bestseller, debuts and ushers in a golden age of TV miniseries (1976)

2 A court in Rome acquits *Last Tango in Paris* director Bernardo Bertolucci and co-stars Marlon Brando and Maria Schneider of obscenity charges (1973)

3 *You Can't Do That on Television*, soon to become Nickelodeon's highest rated series, premieres on a station in Ontario, Canada (1979)

4 George C. Scott is a commanding presence in *Patton*, for which he wins an Oscar that he famously refuses (1970)

5 Rod Stewart prefers blondes — and vice versa, according to the cover story of *People*, as his album *Blondes Have More Fun* suggests (1979)

6 By a nose: PBS debuts Edmond Rostand's classic comedy, *Cyrano de Bergerac,* starring Peter Donat, Marsha Mason and Marc Singer (1974)

7 Mel Brooks is at his peak, petard-hoisting best in the western spoof *Blazing Saddles* with Gene Wilder, Cleavon Little and Madeline Kahn (1974)

FEBRUARY 4, 1974
Celebrity Circus

From unknown, pampered heiress to notorious celebrity bank robber — the strange saga of Patricia Hearst, 19, begins today when she's kidnapped from her Berkeley, CA apartment by an urban guerilla group called the Symbionese Liberation Army. Blanket media coverage erupts as talk of prisoner swaps and ransom swirls. Soon a gun-toting photo and her participation in a bank robbery turn Hearst from kidnapee to fugitive. At trial after her arrest for bank robbery she claims coercion, but famed defense attorney F. Lee Bailey presents a weak case. Convicted, Hearst serves 22 months in prison before being pardoned by President Carter.

"For any victim of a violent crime — when you actually get to go in and see their faces and know that they can't hurt you any more, there is no feeling like that. It finally frees you from a lot of demons."

— PATTY HEARST

February

You talkin' to me? Robert De Niro explodes and implodes in Martin Scorsese's *Taxi Driver*, definitely not to be confused with the 1978 sitcom *Taxi* (1976)

8

Shot on a shoestring budget, Perry Henzell's visceral *The Harder They Come* introduces budding reggae star Jimmy Cliff plus a killer soundtrack with Toots & the Maytals, Desmond Dekker and more (1973)

9

Doonesbury's Andy Lipincott becomes the first cartoon character in a major U.S. comic strip to come out (1976)

10

Partners and politics mix on a presidential eve in Hal Ashby's frothy *Shampoo*, featuring Warren Beatty as a seductive hairdresser (1975)

11

Something sinister lurks behind a blissful suburban façade in *The Stepford Wives*, a chiller based upon Ira Levin's bestseller (1975)

12

So cute, so perky, so melodious – how could the Osmonds from *The Andy Williams Show* ever have *One Bad Apple?* Only as a #1 single (1971)

13

Bob Fosse recreates the magic and decadence of *Cabaret* onscreen, netting Liza Minelli an Oscar in the same year she wins an Emmy for her TV special *Liza With a Z* (1972)

14

FEBRUARY 14, 1972
The Word is... Grease!

Nostalgia has a way of ebbing and flowing, and on this night it becomes a torrent as *Grease* opens at New York's Eden Theater. The circa late '50s rock musical features Barry Bostwick and Carole Demas, and though critics aren't too enthusiastic, the public is. With its angsty, adolescent love, slicked up gangs and class (not classroom) conflict, it's a junior *West Side Story* with a lot less weight but plenty of groovy rock'n'roll. Six years later a movie version, starring John Travolta and Olivia-Newton John, fuels the *Grease* fire.

"As musicals get scarcer, 'Grease' gets better."

—A NEWSPAPER REVIEWER

See More Tales
and Tidbits at
www.365edge.com

15 Curly-locked magician Doug Henning hosts a *World of Magic* special with guests Barbi Benton, Bill Cosby and Melba Moore (1979)

16 David Mamet's tense thieves den, *American Buffalo,* opens on Broadway with Robert Duvall and John Savage (1977)

17 Publisher Ralph Ginzburg, convicted in 1963 of distributing an obscene magazine, *Eros,* through the mails, begins a 3-year jail sentence (1972)

18 Led by idiosyncratic genius Lowell George, Little Feat releases the delicious album *Dixie Chicken,* adding to their esteemed reputation but not helping the band achieve any breakout fame (1973)

19 Stevie Wonder's *Songs In the Key of Life* wins him Grammys for best album and best male pop vocalist (1977)

20 When radio and TV stations are erroneously sent a nuclear alert (instead of a test mode) message, a momentary panic seizes the US (1971)

21 Riding hits like *Proud Mary* and *Bad Moon Rising,* John Fogarty and Creedence Clearwater Revival grace the cover of *Rolling Stone* (1970)

FEBRUARY 15, 1975
Rhythm & Ronstadt

Whatever the style — country, folk, pop standards, R&B, rock, a touch of light opera — Linda Ronstadt always scores big amongst an appreciative public. Today she achieves her only #1 single, *You're No Good,* from her much-praised album *Heart Like A Wheel.* Savvy song selection and a copasetic producer (Peter Asher, once half of the pop British singing duo Peter and Gordon) help the long-haired brunette beauty to not only hit singles like *When Will I Be Loved* and *Heat Wave* but smash albums like *Simple Dreams* and *Living in the USA.* She even dabbles with a stage and screen career in Gilbert and Sullivan's *Pirates of Penzance.*

"The constant fear of a performer is to become what's reflected back at you."

—LINDA RONSTADT

February

Library of Congress: N.Y. World-Telegram & Sun Collection

FEBRUARY 26, 1970
Troubled Times

Simon and Garfunkel's soothing *Bridge Over Troubled Water* soars this day to #1 and holds the spot for six weeks, making it the year's biggest single. But ironically, behind the scenes the duo's tension-ridden professional relationship is crumbling. The recording sessions for the album of the same name prove rocky, as Art Garfunkel is often away filming his debut movie role in Mike Nichols' *Catch-22*. Paul Simon wrote the song (like virtually every S&G song), but later regrets allowing his partner to sing solo. It's the last studio album of new material they'll ever produce.

"It's a Simon and Garfunkel record, but... there are many songs when you don't hear Simon and Garfunkel singing together."
—PAUL SIMON

On the strength of a 3-song demo, rock promoter Bill Graham offers Bruce Springsteen a recording contract but he turns it down (1970)

22

CBS's explosive documentary *The Selling of the Pentagon,* about big business Defense Department connections, debuts (1971)

23

Inspired by a performance of *American Pie* by Don McLean, *Killing Me Softly With His Song* becomes a #1 hit for Roberta Flack (1973)

24

Paul Newman captains a minor league hockey team short on talent but long on fisticuffs in the satiric, slashing *Slap Shot* (1977)

25

The Today Show televises a live kidney transplant, prompting 20,000 people to contact NBC and offer their kidneys for transplant (1975)

26

Conservative Mississippi clergyman Donald Wildmon launches "Turn the Television Off Week" to protest small screen violence (1977)

27

(28th) All dressed up with someplace to go: glam rockers KISS form in NYC (1973)

28/29

the 70s

NOTES

March

1 Stephen Sondheim's *Sweeney Todd* sweeps up after its Broadway debut with eight Tony awards including best musical, actor (Len Cariou) and actress (Angela Lansbury) (1979)

2 Thieves swipe the body of the late Charlie Chaplin from a cemetery in Switzerland; it's discovered in a nearby cornfield two months later (1978)

3 But it's not Frank: Margaret "Hot Lips" Houlihan (Loretta Swit) ties the knot on *M*A*S*H* (1977)

4 Sex, blank and rock'n'roll: the FCC advises radio stations to screen all songs for lyrics that promote or glorify the use of illegal drugs, like *Puff the Magic Dragon* and *White Rabbit* (1971)

5 Disco queen Donna Summer scores with *Heaven Knows,* and soon follows with two #1s: *Hot Stuff* and *Bad Girls* (1979)

6 Robert Redford pays $450,000 for the film rights to *All the President's Men* on the day President Nixon admits that the Watergate burglars were paid hush money (1974)

7 Country sweeps the country as the down home musical/ variety *Hee Haw* lands on the cover of *TV Guide* (1970)

A.B.C.

MARCH 5, 1971
Opposites Attract

After successful runs both on Broadway and in film, Neil Simon's *The Odd Couple* comes to TV with Tony Randall and Jack Klugman, respectively, as the neat and messy apartment mates. However, both stars despise the sitcom's canned laugh track, so ABC agrees to run one show without it. At the end Randall asks for viewer comments, and some 50,000 letters run overwhelming in favor of losing the added laughs. Starting the next season, the show is shot before a live audience with no studio "sweetening." Klugman goes on to win two Emmys for the show, Randall one.

"It took me three hours to figure out 'F.U.' was Felix Unger. It's not your fault, Felix — it's a rotten combination, that's all."

—OSCAR TO FELIX,
  COMPLAINING ABOUT
  HIS NOTES

iStockphoto

MARCH 14, 1972

A Multi-layered *Tapestry*

She'd already had four #1 hits as a songwriter alongside lyricist husband Gerry Goffin, including the Shirelles' *Will You Love Me Tomorrow* and Little Eva's *The Loco-Motion*. After a divorce, Carole King tests out her singing talents too and today wins four Grammys: best female vocalist plus album (*Tapestry*), song (*You've Got A Friend*) and record of the year (*It's Too Late,* with the flip side *I Feel The Earth Move*). Folks seemingly can't go anywhere without hearing the album playing, and it goes on to sell an estimated, extraordinary 22 million copies worldwide.

"A wondrous woven magic, in bits of blue and gold, a tapestry to feel and see, impossible to hold..."

—CAROLE KING

8 Joe Frazier wins a 15-round decision over Muhammad Ali to become world heavyweight champ; each takes home an estimated $2.5 million (1971)

9 A primetime soap depicts troubled relations in *Family,* co-exec produced by noted movie director Mike Nichols (*Catch-22, Silkwood*) (1976)

10 Gloria Gaynor defiantly proclaims *I Will Survive,* the #1 hit in a week where nine of the top ten are disco numbers (1979)

11 Pablo Picasso donates 800 works to a museum in Barcelona, though he hasn't lived in Spain since 1939 when Franco assumed power (1970)

12 A lethal virus, potential nuclear detonation and more in the sci-fi chiller *The Andromeda Strain,* adapted from Michael Crichton's bestseller (1971)

13 Six years after Tyrone Davis's *Turn Back the Hands of Time,* the pop charts do just that as the Four Seasons' *December, 1963 (Oh, What a Night)* hits #1 (1976)

14 *The Burt Bacharach Special,* the first of many from the high-powered composer, features Tom Jones, Rudolph Nureyev and Barbra Streisand (1971)

15
Sexy single gals in the city, a pretend gay roommate (John Ritter) and suggestive situations make *Three's Company* a huge hit (1977)

16
The China Syndrome opens, and 12 days later a reactor malfunction at Three Mile Island in Pennsylvania leads to a near nuclear meltdown (1979)

17
Cracking the closet: Matt Crowley's landmark gay play, *The Boys in the Band*, debuts in a movie version (1970)

18
Out on his own, Canadian rocker Neil Young hits #1 with *Heart of Gold*, aided by Linda Ronstadt and James Taylor on background vocals (1972)

19
Pinball wizardry at the box office as the Who's energetic rock opera *Tommy* hits movie theaters with Eric Clapton, Elton John and Tina Turner (1975)

20
Posthumous perch: the late Janis Joplin scores her only #1 single with the plaintive *Me and Bobby McGee* (1971)

21
After Bob Dylan pleads his cause in *Hurricane (Part I)*, ex-boxer and convicted murderer Rubin "Hurricane" Carter is released from jail for retrial (1976)

U.S. National Archives

MARCH 19, 1979
Politics 24/7

As restrictive federal rules loosen and cable TV begins its rapid growth, cable hits upon a unique programming niche: politics. Created by publishing and political veteran Brian Lamb, and funded entirely by the cable industry, C-SPAN launches live this day to 3.5 million households with a speech by congressman Al Gore. The nonprofit network soon expands its gavel-to-gavel coverage to the Senate, hearings, news conferences, speeches and more, launching two additional channels to blanket the nation's capitol.

"More than anything else, we need in this society the opportunity for people to tell us what they think without being told that they're either dumb, or stupid, or uninformed."

—BRIAN LAMB

Famous high-wire performer Karl Wallenda dies after a 10-story fall from a cable strung between two hotels in San Juan, Puerto Rico (1978) **22**

U.S. National Archives

MARCH 27, 1973
Mob Machinations

Italian-Americans and animal rights groups protested, and the producers received bomb threats. All references to the Mafia were cut from the script. But the rocky start for Francis Ford Coppola's *The Godfather* vanishes on this night as the mob epic wins three top Oscars: best picture, actor and adapted screenplay (co-written by novelist Mario Puzo and Coppola). Marlon Brando boycotts the ceremony, sending an unknown Native American actress to read a statement decrying the industry's treatment of Indians. She's later discovered to be a Mexican actress named Maria Cruz.

"A lawyer with a briefcase can steal more than a hundred men with guns."

—A ROBERT DUVALL LINE
  CUT FROM *THE GODFATHER*,
  MUCH TO HIS CHAGRIN

The Metropolitan Museum of Art opens an exhibition by legendary Spanish couturier Cristóbal Balenciaga, whom Christian Dior once called "the master of us all" (1973) **23**

A fan shrieks "leather," leaps onstage and bites singer Lou Reed in the buttocks at a concert in Buffalo, but the (sore) showman finishes the show (1973) **24**

More than a year in the making, Pink Floyd's landmark conceptual album *Dark Side of the Moon* bows, eventually selling 40+ million (1973) **25**

The first Body Shop opens in the U.K., next to an undertaker that complains to the city council about the name (1976), and grows into an international cosmetics giant **26**

When L.A. traffic delays Charlton Heston, in steps Clint Eastwood on a moment's notice to co-host the Oscars (1973) **27**

Australian Samantha Sang's *Emotion*, written by the Bee Gees' Barry (who also contributes background vocals) and Robin Gibb, goes gold (500,000 units) (1978) **28**

29 Voulez-vous: LaBelle's risqué *Lady Marmalade* hits #1 (1975)

30 When you wish upon a song: Dr. Hook and the Medicine Show's dream (*The Cover of 'Rolling Stone'*) comes true (1973)

31 Unknown Ken Norton defeats former champ Muhammad Ali in a 12- round split decision in San Diego (1973)

Alan Light

MARCH 29, 1977
Rocky's Roots

No one had given ex-liquor salesman and security guard Chuck Wepner much of a shot against Muhammad Ali, but the game contender battled through and lost on a 15th round TKO. Watching that night in 1975 was Sylvester Stallone, then a little known, lightly regarded actor. Within a week the inspired actor had cranked out the screenplay for what would become *Rocky*, a rags-to-riches boxing saga. Tonight it delivered a double Oscar shot, best picture and best director, catapulting Stallone to star status and spawning many sequels.

"The worst thing about fighting is the morning after."

—ROCKY (SYLVESTER STALLONE)

Library of Congress: N.Y. World-Telegram & Sun Collection

April

1 *Cosmopolitan* features a nude centerfold of Burt Reynolds (1972)

2 A naked man streaks across the stage at the Oscars, but it doesn't faze quick-witted presenter David Niven (1974)

3 Button up, or not: Velcro appears on the market (1978)

4 An Elvis Presley concert taped in Hawaii earlier in the year draws a huge TV audience (1973)

5 Aged, painted dame Mae West makes a rare television appearance on a CBS special, *Dick Cavett's Backlot U.S.A.* (1976)

6 After a protracted legal battle, the Smothers Brothers win a $776,300 judgment against CBS for its cancellation of their show back in '69 (1973)

7 Dirty politics still grip America as Redford/Hoffman's *All the President's Men* debuts, with an Oscar-winning screenplay by William Goldman (1976)

iStockphoto

APRIL 1, 1979
And A Child Shall Lead

Before CNN, ESPN, Discovery, USA or most any other cable network (except for HBO and WTBS), there was Nickelodeon. Owned by Warner Cable, it beamed kids programming to its 600,000 home system in Columbus, Ohio. Today it went national with one original series, *Pinwheel,* interspersing puppets and live actors with acquired cartoons. A noncommercial goodwill tool to help cablers win franchises and subscribers, it made a savvy move in 1980 by hiring Geraldine Laybourne. She discovered early original hits like *You Can't Do That on Television* (from Canada) and *Double Dare,* made the controversial call to accept ads in 1984, and laid the groundwork for its long-term success.

"I don't think it would be an exaggeration to call Nickelodeon revolutionary... Nickelodeon the television network has a stronger artistic identity than most television shows."

— CATHLEEN SCHINE

April

APRIL 14, 1973
Heavy Breathy

When Johnny Rivers sang *Mountain of Love* in 1964, he wasn't referring to Barry White, but he could have been. That year the 300-pound producer tasted his first success with *Harlem Shuffle*, a hit for the duo Bob and Earl. He later created a sexy female trio, Love Unlimited, and wrote them a million seller. Then he unleashed his own rich baritone, steamy lyrics and his 40-piece Love Unlimited Orchestra to deliver a torrent of lush hits like *Never, Never Gonna Give Ya Up*, *Can't Get Enough of Your Love, Babe* and, today, *I'm Gonna Love You Just A Little More Baby*. The big man always preferred the appellation "prophet of love."

"'Cause I found what the world is searching for, here, right here, my dear, I don't have to look no more..."

— BARRY WHITE

8 The FCC and outside pressure groups force the broadcast networks into making 8–9 p.m. a family hour with little sex or violence, and ratings soon tumble (1975)

9 Superhawk (and very ill) John Wayne shows true grit, presenting the best picture Oscar to the anti-war *The Deer Hunter* (1979), whose director (Michael Cimino) segues to the disastrous *Heaven's Gate*

10 In London, Paul McCartney announces he is leaving the Beatles for "personal differences, business differences, musical differences" (1970)

11 Borscht belt love and life lessons for a young Richard Dreyfuss in the wry *The Apprenticeship of Duddy Kravitz* (1974)

12 The period coming-of-age drama *Summer of '42* debuts, preceded by a best-selling novel that was actually an adaptation of the screenplay (1971)

13 Crashingly loud heavy metal rockers Led Zeppelin specialize in albums, not singles, but today their biggest tune, *Whole Lotta Love*, goes gold (500,000 units) (1970)

14 Four years after their first #1, *Black Water*, the Doobie Brothers reclaim the top spot with their biggest single ever, *What A Fool Believes* (1979)

15 Clint Eastwood's inclusion of Roberta Flack's *The First Time Ever I Saw Your Face* in his directorial debut, *Play Misty For Me*, helps it hit #1 (1972)

16 *Rolling Stone* catches up with bad boy cover boy Dennis Hopper on the set of *The Last Movie* (1970)

17 Gerald Ford becomes the first president to attend a performance at the Ford Theater since the 1865 assassination of President Lincoln (1975)

18 Alice Cooper stars alongside horror veteran Vincent Price in *The Nightmare*, a TV special inspired by his *Welcome To My Nightmare* album (1975)

19 Seven weeks after a near-fatal heart attack, Martin Sheen returns to the Philippines to resume filming *Apocalypse Now*, Francis Ford Coppola's tempestuous, troubled take on the Vietnam War (1977)

20 *Sticky Fingers*, the new Rolling Stones album, features a cover designed by Andy Warhol with an actual working jeans zipper (1971)

21 The Tony awards come out tomorrow: *Annie* opens on Broadway, and the season's musical smash goes on to win seven Tony and Drama Desk Awards (1977)

Library of Congress: N.Y. World-Telegram & Sun Collection

APRIL 20, 1977
Allen Arrives with Annie

After a half dozen films Woody Allen delivers *Annie Hall,* his best to date (and some say best ever). Mixing his trademark riffs on life, death, sex, angst and neuroses, it does big box-office business and wins four Oscars: best actress (Diane Keaton), director (Allen), original screenplay (Allen and Marshall Brickman) and the top prize, best picture, over the favored *Star Wars.* Yet Woody's an Oscar no-show; instead, he's playing clarinet at Michael's Pub with the New Orleans Funeral and Ragtime Orchestra, his regular Monday night gig. The film also inspires an anti-style fashion trend, based on the ditzy title character's kooky look mixing men's clothes, grandma's clothes and floppy hats.

"I couldn't let down the guys."

—WOODY ALLEN EXPLAINING WHY HE MISSED THE OSCAR CEREMONY

APRIL 26, 1978

Disco Decadence

Over half a century the property had variously housed opera, theatre, radio and TV productions, but none of its previous lives could ever match its fame and status when, on this day, Studio 54 opened. No disco more embodied the hedonistic, heady days of the late '70s and '80s than Studio 54 and its non-stop mix of sex, drugs and alcohol — imbibed to a nonstop disco beat and dazzling light show. Run by flamboyant Steve Rubell and silent partner Ian Schrager, it famously attracted a who's who of celebrities from Alvin Ailey (whose troupe performed on opening night) to Andy Warhol. The party lasted eight years.

"Seriously, it was insane. I remember the lights and the energy. There was no vibe to describe the funhouse in Manhattan."

—A STUDIO 54 DEVOTEE

22 ABC lures Barbara Walters from NBC with a $1 million contract and makes her the first female anchor of a network evening newscast (1976)

23 Primal fear erupts in James Dickey's novel *Deliverance*, which he later adapts into a harrowing movie directed by John Boorman (1970)

24 Dorothy Hamill's *Corner of the Sky* finds the champion figure skater returning to her hometown for a nostalgic television special (1979)

25 Instituting its most sweeping rules changes since 1933, the NFL moves goalposts to the back line and introduces sudden death in case of a tie (1974)

26 *Ringo*, an updated TV version of *The Prince and the Pauper*, features the ex-Beatle with a little help from his friends Angie Dickinson, Carrie Fisher, John Ritter, Vincent Price and George Harrison (1978)

27 All eyes turn to the deep blue yonder as America's fifth mission to the moon, *Apollo 16*, splashes down (1972)

28 Based on a character created by underground comics legend R. Crumb, *Fritz the Cat*, the first X-rated cartoon movie, premieres (1972)

29 Raucous rockers Cheap Trick follow up their hypnotic *Surrender* with their first top ten hit, *I Want You To Want Me* (1979)

30 Porn star Harry Reems is convicted in Memphis federal court of distributing the film *Deep Throat* across state lines (1976)

NOTES

APRIL 30, 1975
Chaotic Collapse

After years of bloodshed and strife and protest, the Vietnam War closes as Saigon falls to the Viet Cong. Americans at home watch a tumultuous, ignominious end unfold on the roof of the U.S. Embassy. Panic and desperation collide as army helicopters come and go, ferrying out American civilians, soldiers and some Vietnamese. Thousands of their frantic countrymen swarm into the compound in hopes of fleeing, but are left abandoned and angry. A few eyewitness journalists and missionaries remain when the South Vietnamese government unconditionally surrenders at 10:02 a.m. Saigon time.

"Today [we] have concluded an agreement to end the war and bring peace with honor in Vietnam and in Southeast Asia."

—PRESIDENT RICHARD NIXON

May

1 The Pulitzers raise eyebrows by giving prizes to columnist Jack Anderson and *The New York Times* for their roles in the release of the Pentagon Papers (1972)

2 Black, wild and...: no-holds or language-barred Richard Pryor breaks through with his landmark album, *That Nigger's Crazy* (1974)

3 Do I hear...? Auctioneers sell off 45 years' worth of MGM costumes and props, including Judy Garland's ruby red slippers, for a total take of $7 mil (1970)

4 A most unlikely 2-fer: heavy metal rockers Grand Funk hit #1 with *The Loco-Motion* (1974), a blistering remake of Little Eva's original #1 from '62

5 Ice cream dream: in a converted gas station in Burlington, Vermont, a national obsession dawns: Ben & Jerry's Homemade Ice Cream (1978)

6 An electrical fire causes $3 million in damages at Goldwyn's Hollywood studio and Steve McQueen, rehearsing for his role as a fire chief in *The Towering Inferno*, dons gear and helps put it out (1974)

7 The Eagles and *Rolling Stone* magazine staffers play softball to determine if the group will do an interview, and the Eagles win 15-8; no interview (1978)

Library of Congress: N.Y. World-Telegram & Sun Collection

MAY 4, 1970
Four Dead in Ohio

Inflamed by President Nixon's announcement of the invasion of Cambodia, anti-Vietnam War protests are at fever pitch. Violence and tensions run high as student strikes shut down hundreds of colleges and high schools nationwide. On this day, after dispersing yet another rally, panicked Ohio National Guardsmen suddenly fire at students more than 250 feet away. Four die — two protesters, and two students simply walking to classes. A student photojournalist captures the shocking horror in a shot seen 'round the world, amplifying both U.S. and world opposition to the war.

"The Kent State tragedy must mark the last time that, as a matter of course, loaded rifles are issued to guardsmen confronting student demonstrators."

—THE PRESIDENT'S COMMISSION ON CAMPUS UNREST

MAY 9, 1974

Star Sighting

On this balmy spring evening in Cambridge, Massachusetts, a legend is born. Amongst a crowd attending a Bonnie Raitt concert at a sold-out Harvard Square Theatre is local rock critic Jon Landau, who's blown away by an opening act whose first two Columbia albums had generated lackluster sales. But onstage the band performs songs from their then-unreleased *Born to Run*. Landau eventually comes aboard to co-produce, and a year later the new album catapults Bruce Springsteen to fame. He soon becomes the only rock star to grace *Time* and *Newsweek* covers in the same week. The Boss's warm-up days are over.

"I saw rock'n'roll future, and its name is Bruce Springsteen."

—JON LANDAU

---

8 End of an era: the Beatles release their final album, *Let it Be,* remixed by producer Phil Spector (1970)

9 Exuberant black musical *Ain't Misbehavin',* featuring the music of Fats Waller, opens on Broadway en route to 1,604 performances (1978)

10 NHL player of the year Bobby Orr scores 40 seconds into OT, giving the Boston Bruins their first Stanley Cup title since 1941 (1970)

11 Fresh off a worldwide tour to promote *Tommy,* the Who release the scorching album *Live at Leeds,* recorded at university there (1970)

12 Mick Jagger marries Bianca Perez Morena de Macias, daughter of a Nicaraguan diplomat, in St. Tropez, France (1971); they divorce seven years later

13 She's probably not *Pretty As You Feel*: Grace Slick crashes her Mercedes in S.F., forcing the Jefferson Airplane to postpone its recording session (1971)

14 *The Happy Hooker,* a screen adaptation of Xaviera Hollander's bestseller about her exploits as a NYC madam, opens (1975)

15 Long-haired heavy metal rockers Black Sabbath, purposely heavy on dark lyrics, release their self-titled debut album, *Black Sabbath* (1970)

16 Robert Altman's anarchic black comedy *M*A*S*H* wins the Grand Prix at the Cannes Film Festival, latter snagging an Oscar for best screenplay (1970)

U.S. National Archives

MAY 17, 1973
Here, Hearings

Less than a year earlier, Washington, D.C. police had arrested five men for breaking into the offices of the Democratic National Committee. A firestorm quickly erupted and, on this day, the sordid, once covert affair burst onto TV. The U.S. Senate hearings, shown live, revealed an astonishing secret: the existence of a system that automatically taped everything said in the Oval Office. The dominos began falling, culminating in President Nixon's resignation 15 months later. An unprecedented 85% of Americans tuned in to at least part of the blockbuster Watergate coverage.

"What did the president know, and when did he know it?"

—SENATOR HOWARD BAKER (R-TENNESSEE)

17 Blacklisted screenwriter Dalton Trumbo finally receives his Oscar for *The Brave One*, awarded in 1957 to a pseudonymous "Robert Rich" (1975)

18 Teen heartthrob Leif Garrett hosts his only TV variety special on CBS with guests Bob Hope, Marie Osmond, Brooke Shields and Flip Wilson (1979)

19 Millionairess Sandra West, 37, is buried in San Antonio according to her wishes: dressed in a lace nightgown and seated in her baby blue 1964 Ferrari (1977)

20 The Beatles' documentary *Let It Be* debuts simultaneously in Liverpool and London, hinting at the group's unraveling and later winning an Oscar for original song score (1970)

21 Think pink: Peter Sellers reprises one of his most famous roles, bumbling Inspector Clouseau, in Blake Edwards' *Return of the Pink Panther* (1975)

See More Tales
and Tidbits at
www.365edge.com

Alan Light

Mark Hamill, a.k.a.
Luke Skywalker

MAY 25, 1977
Action, Thrills and
Sky Adventure

There are box office hits, there
are blockbusters — and then
there's *Star Wars*. Released this
day, George Lucas's elaborately
entertaining sci-fi saga catapults
into cinematic history. Jam-packed
with villains and heroes and aliens
and robots and state-of-the-art
f/x, *Star Wars* obliterates box-office
records. The good-versus-evil
interplanetary adventure wins
instant, eternal fame, a half dozen
Oscars, and spurs a franchise
of epic proportions — all from a
modest budget of $11 million.
And a fertile imagination.

"A long time ago in a galaxy
far, far away..."

—THE OPENING OF
  STAR WARS

Meatloaf's classic album *Bat Out of Hell,* honed by producer Jim Steinman, goes gold (500,000 units) and will keep soaring into multi-platinum (14 million units) stratosphere (1978)

22

Sam Peckinpah disowns a truncated *Pat Garrett and Billy the Kid,* but the studio later releases a director's cut that elevates the hard-bitten western's reputation (1973)

23

Jazz giant Duke Ellington, recently awarded the Presidential Medal of Freedom and France's Legion of Honor, passes away (1974)

24

Intrepid Ellen Ripley (Sigourney Weaver), no relation to Eleanor Rigby, battles an outer space monster that's hard to stomach in Ridley Scott's *Alien* (1979)

25

Monster guitar riffs from the Edgar Winter Group blast to the top of the pop charts with *Frankenstein* (1973)

26

Liverpool's Cavern Club, where the Beatles performed 282 times and were discovered by Brian Epstein, is razed and replaced by a shopping center (1973)

27

After an analysis of TV ads shows women overwhelmingly in household or subservient roles, NOW facetiously reports women's "extraordinary incompetence is exceeded only by their monumental stupidity" (1972)

28

29 Universal Studios stages a 14-hour marathon poker match at famed eatery Chasen's to promote its reissue of the Redford/Newman con test *The Sting* (1977)

30 Jimi Hendrix plays at the Berkeley Community Theatre, one of his last live gigs (1970)

31 What's Ahead For TV? *Newsweek* posits that question in a cover story (1971)

NOTES

iStockphoto

MAY 31, 1971
An Unexpected Trip

Many bands have fans. A few generate fanatics. But none have ever attracted a more loyal, devoted (some say crazed) following than the Grateful Dead. The acid rock/psychedelic pioneers begin coalescing in San Francisco in 1965, producing a hybrid country rock sound, legendarily long concerts and a decidedly non-mainstream reputation. The band eschews singles and makes its name on albums like *Workingman's Dead* and *American Beauty.* On this day, 36 deadheads at a concert in the Winterland Ballroom are treated after unwittingly drinking LSD-laced cider.

"Lately it occurs to me, what a long, strange trip it's been."

— *TRUCKIN'*

June

1 A few months after the death of Tammi Terrell, his beloved singing partner, Marvin Gaye mines his spiritual side for a topical societal masterpiece, *What's Going On* (1970)

2 Amsterdam's Van Gogh Museum begins daily playings of Don McLean's *Vincent*, the follow-up to his mammoth #1, *American Pie* (1972)

3 I'll take you where? All the way to #1, where the Staple Singers arrive with their bluesy, gospel-tinged *I'll Take You There* (1972)

4 In their first U.S. tour since Altamont, the Rolling Stones open to huge crowds in Seattle with a new warm-up act: 22-year-old Stevie Wonder (1972)

5 One hit does not a series star make: the *Ode to Billie Joe* singer proves it in the couple of weeks' run of a musical variety, *Bobbie Gentry's Happiness* (1974)

6 Smooth soul singer Curtis Mayfield, off last year's two top ten hits, *Freddie's Dead* and *Superfly*, double dips with two albums going gold (500,000 units): *Curtis* and *Back to the World* (1973)

7 Dr. Timothy Leary, the Harvard psychiatrist turned drug guru, is released from prison for a 1970 narcotics conviction after the parole board reverses an earlier decision denying him parole (1976)

iStockphoto

JUNE 5, 1971
Killer TV

On this day health food enthusiast and entrepreneur Jerome Rodale, 72, tapes an appearance on *The Dick Cavett Show*. Fresh off a *New York Times* magazine cover story calling him the "guru of the organic food cult," the organic gardening proponent and publisher boasts he'll "live to 100 unless I'm run down by some sugar-crazed taxi driver." After his interview, as Cavett talks politics with journalist Pete Hamill, he appears to nod off. "Are we boring you?" quips the host. But Rodale isn't asleep. He's dead, killed by a heart attack. The show never airs.

"A genius, say Rodale admirers. A crackpot, say his detractors."

— WADE GREENE

June

Classically trained keyboardist Rick Wakeman departs Yes, goes the solo route but winds up reuniting from time to time over the years (1974)

8

Adam Macmaster

CBS Records signs up a promising young singer named Bruce Springsteen to a ten-album deal with a $25,000 advance (1972)

9

JUNE 11, 1975
Country Classic

Conventional film wisdom suggests that American audiences prefer a single protagonist and a straightforward storyline. Iconoclastic Robert Altman tosses that wisdom overboard and creates *Nashville*, a multi-layered tableau of competing country music stars, their families, wannabes and assorted hangers-on. Joan Tewkesbury's inspired script intertwines these diverse, disparate lives with often improvised dialogue by a stellar ensemble cast — Lily Tomlin, Ned Beatty, Allen Garfield, Keith Carradine and Karen Black to name but a few — and a toe-tapping original country soundtrack. It's a nuanced cinematic tour de force whose power remains undiminished.

"One of the most ambitious, and more artistically successful 'backstage' musical dramas yet made... One of Altman's best films."
— VARIETY

More inspired inanity from Woody Allen with *Love and Death*, a spoof of Russian films and literature (1975)

10

Annie Leibovitz shoots the cover of *Rolling Stone*, not her usual celebrity image but a shot of anti-war activists as the Vietnam War roils America (1970)

11

Marlon Brando breaks the jaw of notorious paparazzi photographer Ron Galella (1973)

12

A tug-of-war between 2,200 students and teachers at a Harrisonburg, PA middle school attempting to set a world record ends with 70 injured when the 2,000-foot nylon rope breaks (1978)

13

Dr. Henry M. Heimlich gives a public demonstration of his now famous, life-saving maneuver to dislodge items trapped in the windpipe (1974)

14

15 An evangelical rally in Texas attracts 75,000, prompting Rev. Billy Graham to call it a "religious Woodstock" (1972)

16 The first UPC scanner goes into operation at a supermarket in Troy, Ohio, and customers gripe that products no longer have prices on them (1972)

17 In its eighth season, *Fiddler on the Roof* becomes the longest-running show in Broadway history to date with its 3,225th performance (1972)

18 Fleetwood Mac delivers its only #1 single, *Dreams*, from its smash album *Rumours* (1977)

19 Hockey legend Gordy Howe comes out of retirement to sign with the WHA's Houston Aeros, along with sons Mark and Marty, for $1 million (1973)

20 Roman Polanski spins a convoluted film noir, *Chinatown*, with star turns by Jack Nicholson, Faye Dunaway and John Huston (1974)

21 More than a year before its Broadway debut, Andrew Lloyd Webber's stunning *Evita* opens to full houses in London (1978)

iStockphoto

JUNE 20, 1975
Hark! A Shark

At the time, the young director had only one feature film to his credit, the modestly successful *The Sugarland Express.* But on this day his next film steered his career straight into the fast lane. Steven Spielberg's *Jaws* successfully tapped into one of man's primal fears — what's lurking beneath the surface of the water? — and took a gigantic chomp out of the box-office. This being Hollywood, lesser sequels soon surfaced but Spielberg was onto far more momentous fare, movies like *Close Encounters of the Third Kind, Raiders of the Lost Ark* and *E.T. — The Extra-Terrestrial.*

"This is a not a boat accident, and it wasn't any propeller. It wasn't any coral reef, and it wasn't Jack the Ripper. It was a shark."

— MARINE BIOLOGIST MATT HOOPER (RICHARD DREYFUSS)

Alan Light

JUNE 23, 1978

Echoes of Janis

At L.A.'s Wiltern Theatre, Bette Midler performs to a packed house. But it's not her usual "Divine Miss M" persona — it's hard rock from the hard-livin', Janis Joplin-inspired title character of *The Rose*. Director Mark Rydell tells the crowd, "You look sensational. We are going to photograph you, so stay vital, stay alive." Led by Oscar-winning cinematographer Vilmos Zsigmond, seven cameras capture the raw, raucous night. The haunting title track hits #3 on the pop charts, and Midler earns an Oscar nomination for best supporting actress in her film debut.

"People say to me, 'Rose, when was the first time you heard the blues?' And I always say, 'Honey, the day I was born.'"

—BETTE MIDLER IN *THE ROSE*

22

Jim Henson's cuddly creations fill the screen in their first theatrical, with Kermit, Miss Piggy et al starring in *The Muppet Movie* (1979)

23

Jane Fonda winds up winning an Oscar for the call girl role Barbra Streisand rejected in *Klute*, a murder mystery with Donald Sutherland (1971)

24

Dennis Hopper sues Peter Fonda for three percent of the profits of *Easy Rider* for his contribution to the screenplay (1970)

25

Where Satan's offspring goes, gore's sure to follow in Richard Donner's horror/suspense summertime smash, *The Omen* (1975)

26

The Big Apple opens its now famed TKTS half price theater ticket booth at 47th & Broadway, and soon dual lines extend around the block every day (1973)

27

To capitalize on the *Star Wars*-inspired sci-fi craze, *Moonraker's* producers add outer space elements for jet-setting 007, Roger Moore (1979)

28

During a Tigers/Yankees game ABC calls Detroit's 21-year-old rookie phenom Mark "The Bird" Fidrych "the most interesting player since Dizzy Dean," but wildness soon ends his brief career (1976)

29 Charlton Heston is long gone, but Roddy McDowell's still around in *Conquest of the Planet of the Apes,* the third sequel in the popular primate franchise (1972)

30 Three days after her divorce from Sonny is finalized, Cher marries rocker Duane Allman (1975), embarking on a rocky four-year marriage

NOTES

iStockphoto

JUNE 29, 1972
Slopes to Screen

Continuing a string of box office hits like *Downhill Racer* and *Butch Cassidy and the Sundance Kid,* Robert Redford opens in a thought-provoking political drama, *The Candidate.* He invests some earnings in a Colorado ski resort and renames it Sundance. A few years later an independent film festival debuts in Salt Lake City with films like *Midnight Cowboy* and *Mean Streets.* Intrigued, Redford soon provides backing and so begins the Sundance Film Festival, an offshoot of his Sundance Institute that goes on to become one of the world's most renowned, successful places to nurture independent film talent.

"I think the environment should be put in the category of our national security. Defense of our resources is just as important as defense abroad. Otherwise what is there to defend?"

—ROBERT REDFORD

July

1 A triangular love affair amongst Glenda Jackson, Peter Finch and Murray Head plus full frontal male nudity make for a sensationalistic *Sunday Bloody Sunday* (1971)

2 Cool private eye John Shaft (Richard Roundtree) investigates to the strains of Isaac Hayes' Oscar-winning score in *Shaft* (1971)

3 On the strength of the #1 smash *Tie A Yellow Ribbon 'Round the Old Oak Tree,* the musical variety *Tony Orlando and Dawn* debuts on ABC (1974)

4 Flush with *The Thrill is Gone,* his biggest single ever, B.B. King plays the Atlanta Pop Festival with Jimi Hendrix, Jethro Tull and Johnny Winter (1970)

5 Celebs like Raquel Welch and Farrah Fawcett threaten to sue the Rolling Stones for their altered faces on the group's album cover of *Some Girls* (1978)

6 Shrinking sweets: with the price of sugar rising, Lifesavers enlarges their candy's holes and Necco wafers reduce their diameter from 1-1/2" to 7/8" (1974)

7 *Grease* is not only the word but a smash film version of the Broadway play, featuring Frankie Valle's title track that hits #1 on the pop charts (1978)

Library of Congress: N.Y. World-Telegram & Sun Collection

JULY 3, 1971
Born to be Wild

Doors' front man Jim Morrison led a turbulent life. His L.A.-based band, two years after forming in 1965, topped the singles charts with *Light My Fire* and *Hello, I Love You.* Strong albums cemented their reputation as fiery, anti-establishment warriors. For Morrison that included several high-profile arrests: one after a gig in Miami for exposing himself and simulating masturbation, and another for public drunkenness and interfering with a flight. Morrison bolted for Paris where he wrote poetry, released a book and, on this day, died a mysterious death in his apartment's bathtub. His Paris gravesite, near those of Oscar Wilde, Edith Piaf and Frederic Chopin, has become a forever shrine.

"I'm interested in anything about revolt, disorder, chaos, especially activity that appears to have no meaning. It seems to me to be the road toward freedom."

—JIM MORRISON

Ueli Frey

JULY 11, 1973
Reggae Roots

On a hot summer night a line snakes down Boylston Street in downtown Boston. "Who're you seein'?" calls out a passerby. "The Wailers," answers a fan. "The gah-den's thataway," the passerby replies facetiously, referring to the Boston Garden and the Hartford Whalers. The masses haven't yet heard of the dreadlocked Jamaican reggae band and its superstar, Bob Marley, but the cognoscenti have. Fans pack five sold-out shows at Boston's small, legendary club Paul's Mall. Amidst a thick backstage smell of ganja and the sweet backing harmonies of the I-Threes (Judy Mowatt, Marcia Griffiths and Bob's wife, Rita), the Wailers tear up the joint with their distinctive roots, rock and reggae beat – one that the world's soon to discover and embrace.

"One good thing about music, when it hits you feel no pain."

—BOB MARLEY

A rainy 2-day concert at the Pocono Raceway, the biggest since Woodstock, draws 200,000 fans (at $11 each) for Three Dog Night, J. Geils Band, Rod Stewart and more (1972)

8

Propelled by the hit *Brown Eyed Girl*, British singer/songwriter Van Morrison, ex-front man for Them (*Gloria*), makes the cover of *Rolling Stone* (1970)

9

The offbeat *Greaser's Palace,* the second film from iconoclastic Robert Downey, Sr. (yes, Robert Downey Jr.'s pop), opens (1972)

10

Winding up its long fish-out-of-water run, the *Beverly Hillbillies'* cast moves onto the cover page of *TV Guide* (1970)

11

Disco inferno: a rock deejay's promotional stunt, blowing up a crate of disco records, triggers a riot and forces cancellation of the second game of a Chicago White Sox/Detroit Tigers doubleheader (1979)

12

Eric Clapton releases his version of reggae star Bob Marley's *I Shot the Sheriff,* which shoots to #1 (1974)

13

During her trip to North Vietnam, which earned her the undying enmity of many, Jane Fonda makes a broadcast over Radio Hanoi (1972)

14

July the **70**s

15 Sarasota news anchor Chris Chubbuck announces an attempted suicide, pulls out a .38 revolver and fatally shoots herself in the head (1974)

16 WCBS-FM becomes the first major radio station to switch to a solid gold format, and soon stations nationwide are leaping onto the oldies bandwagon (1972)

17 Canadian Alex Trebek makes his American game show debut as host and title character of a short-lived quiz show, *The Wizard of Odds* (1973)

18 Unpretentious sleeper *Breaking Away,* about four bicycle racing college pals, wins an Oscar for its script and becomes one of year's surprise hits (1979)

19 When residents of Wildwood, NJ try to impose a dress code prompted by tourists wearing skimpy bathing suits, the ACLU disagrees (1978)

20 Turning Japanese: McDonald's opens its first restaurant in Japan, and two months later so does Dunkin' Donuts (1971)

21 The FTC accuses McDonald's of distributing only $13,000 of an announced $500,000 sweepstakes contest (1970)

JULY 21, 1973
Short Success

Curly-haired Jim Croce, sporting a thick Fu Manchu moustache, had kicked around a lot of odd jobs — day laborer, radio ad salesman, truck driver — while nursing his musical dreams. Working as a telephone lineman, he'd encountered a belligerent co-worker who became the inspiration for *Bad, Bad Leroy Brown,* which hit #1 today and ignited his career. The years of struggle had paid off, and amidst a heavy touring schedule he soon released his third album, *I Got a Name.* Late that September, following a college concert in Louisiana, he boarded a private plane that crashed upon takeoff. Croce was 30.

"I'm a kind of music psychologist, or a musical bouncer, or a live juke box. It depends on the audience."

—JIM CROCE

JULY 26, 1973
Exit the Dragon

Bruce Lee's best movie, *Enter the Dragon* debuts today, too late for the popular martial arts master to enjoy. He died a week earlier under mysterious circumstances at his Hong Kong mistress's house. Lee had parlayed his martial arts skills, honed by exhaustive training, along with good looks and a charismatic personality, to the brink of stardom. From behind-the-scenes training of people like Steve McQueen and Kareem Abdul-Jabbar, Lee had leapt to TV as Kato on *The Green Hornet* and into a run of successful kung fu flicks. He lives on forever as an influential and iconic pop culture hero.

"Showing off is the fool's idea of glory."

—BRUCE LEE

See More Tales
and Tidbits at
www.365edge.com

Unpredictable, wild-eyed rocker Ian Anderson of Jethro Tull gets the cover treatment in *Rolling Stone* as *Aqualung* makes waves (1971) **22**

The smiley, melodic brother and sister duo, the Carpenters, score their first #1 single with *(They Long to Be) Close to You* (1970) **23**

Vicarious vigilante justice fans make Charles Bronson's *Death Wish* one of the year's biggest films (1974), with inferior sequels soon to follow **24**

Broadway musicals don't get much bigger than *A Chorus Line,* which opens and later sweeps nine Tony awards plus a Pulitzer (1975) **25**

Anne Baxter, who'd played one role in the movie *All About Eve,* steps into another in the Broadway version, *Applause,* replacing Tony winner Lauren Bacall (1971) **26**

After a 3-year legal battle, former Beatle John Lennon wins formal permission to remain in the U.S. as a permanent resident (1976) **27**

Toga! Toga! John Belushi, Tim Matheson and their frat brothers party on in *National Lampoon's Animal House* (1978) **28**

29 Alvin Toffler's *Future Shock* rocks the country with its prediction of "shattering stress and disorientation" due to the rapid pace of technological and societal change (1970)

30 Prime Minister Charles de Gaulle winds up in the crosshairs of wily assassin Edward Fox in the pulse pounding movie *Day of the Jackal,* based on the Frederick Forsyth bestseller (1973)

31 New wave punk rockers The Clash debut their first album in the U.S., two years after its U.K. release, and soon comes *London Calling* (1979)

NOTES

JULY 31, 1971
Sweet Baby James

Long-haired, handsome James Taylor stares out pensively from the cover of his debut album, *Sweet Baby James.* But his angelic look belies an inner turmoil: heroin addiction, rehab and the suicide of a friend that he blends into *Fire and Rain,* the breakout single that reaches #3. On this day J.T. tops the charts with *You've Got A Friend,* written by his friend Carole King, and his life turns around: TV appearances, the cover of *Time* magazine, sold-out tours and a backstage meeting with Carly Simon, whom he marries the following year.

"I'm probably genetically predisposed to substance abuse, so I didn't stand a chance. It felt like it solved all kinds of problems for me."

—JAMES TAYLOR

August

1 Money and hair prove the right combination to revive the musical variety with the debut of *The Sonny and Cher Comedy Hour* (1971)

2 Laying unreleased for two years, an edgy, intense *Performance*, featuring the film debut of Mick Jagger, opens (1970)

3 Written by a former Dallas Cowboys' wide receiver, *North Dallas Forty* delivers gridiron action on and more action off the field (1979)

4 A fundraiser at the Forum in L.A. for the family of the late Lowell George includes the remaining members of Little Feat plus Jackson Browne, Emmylou Harris, Bonnie Raitt and Linda Ronstadt (1979)

5 Dan Aykroyd and John Belushi guest star on NBC's *The Beach Boys Special,* the first of the group's many specials over the next decade (1976)

6 Hippies and yippies invade Disneyland and create a raucous, rather un-family friendly scene (1970)

7 Faye Dunaway ties the knot (for the first time) with Peter Wolf, lead singer of the Boston-based J. Geils Band (1974)

Library of Congress: N.Y. World-Telegram & Sun Collection

AUGUST 1, 1971
Introducing the Celebrity Fundraiser

A modern day Robin Hood, George Harrison doesn't steal from the rich to give to the poor — he taps the rich to contribute their talents to help the poor for free. Tonight's *Concert for Bangladesh* at Madison Square Garden, to benefit needy refugees in East Pakistan, features a stellar lineup including Badfinger, Eric Clapton, Billy Preston, Leon Russell, Ravi Shankar and Bob Dylan, who shows up unannounced to play his first concert in two years. The most prominent no-show? John Lennon, who'd agreed to play solo as Harrison had asked — until Yoko found out. The event provides UNICEF with an immediate $250,000 relief check, with more coming from future recording revenues.

"It really made the show... Bob [Dylan] just gave it that extra bit of clout."

—GEORGE HARRISON

iStockphoto

AUGUST 13, 1977
Sweet Success

Her husband's business associates raved about her tasty cookies. You should open a store, they said. But such individual praise flew in the face of conventional wisdom that suggested no business could survive just selling cookies. Up for the challenge, entrepreneurial 20-year-old Debra "Debbi" Fields opened Mrs. Field's Chocolate Chippery in Palo Alto, California today. And despite all odds her cookies, brownies and muffins launched a worldwide success. Another purveyor of sweet tooth satisfaction launched in the '70s too, Famous Amos Chocolate Chip Cookies.

"When you buy a cookie baked on the premises with only natural ingredients, you feel like you're doing something good for yourself."

— BUSINESS PROFESSOR
  DAVID WEINSTEIN

An estimated 100 million watch live as besieged President Richard Nixon, facing impeachment, announces his resignation (1974)

8

Janis Joplin buys a headstone for blues singer Bessie Smith, who died following a car crash in 1937 after being turned away from a whites-only hospital (1970)

9

First Lady Betty Ford reveals on *60 Minutes* that all her children have tried marihuana, and that the Supreme Court made a "great decision" in legalizing abortion (1975)

10

Summer fades but nostalgia endures with the premiere of *American Graffiti*, George Lucas' big pre-*Star Wars* hit (1973)

11

Twenty-eight hours after artist Christo hangs a 400-foot, 6-ton orange curtain across Rifle Gap in Colorado, 60 m.p.h. winds tear it and force its removal (1972)

12

Yankees' announcer Phil Rizzuto lends some play-by-play verisimilitude to Meatloaf's horny teen anthem, *Paradise By the Dashboard Light* (1978)

13

Sam Peckinpah's moody macho movie *Bring Me the Head of Alfredo Garcia* features Warren Oates and Kris Kristofferson (1974)

14

15 The U.S. Civil Rights Commission issues a study charging TV programming with perpetuating racial and sexual stereotypes (1977)

16 The Ramones begin a residency at the small, ultra hip NYC club, CBGB's (1974)

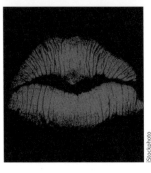

iStockphoto

17 Eric Clapton's *461 Ocean Boulevard,* named after the Miami studio where it was recorded, tops the album charts for the first of four weeks (1974)

AUGUST 14, 1975
Midnight Madness

After a successful stage run in London for a couple years, the musical inspired a movie version. Okay, nothing so unusual about that — but then all madness broke loose, and hasn't stopped since. The sci-fi-comedy-musical-horror hyphenate that is the *Rocky Horror Picture Show* stands alone in the annals of cult movie classics. Midnight screenings attract fans dressed as their favorite characters, bringing appropriate props, shouting out lines and generally cavorting and carousing. They affectionately refer to themselves as sluts, as opposed to virgins (who've never seen the movie). Who's bringing the rice?

18 The King's Procession: all eyes turn to Memphis for the funeral of Elvis Presley, who died two days before at age 42 (1977)

19 Super swimmer Mark Spitz graces the cover of *Life* magazine's Olympic preview, foreshadowing the record-shattering seven gold medals he'll win in Munich (1972)

"I would like, if I may, to take you on a strange journey."

—THE CRIMINOLOGIST (CHARLES GRAY)

20 Four days after Elvis Presley's death, Ballantine Books announces a two million print run, its largest ever, for Steve Dunleavy's *Elvis: What Happened?* (1977)

21 The Charlie Daniels Band strikes gold (500,000 units) with its fast-fiddlin' hit *The Devil Went Down to Georgia* (1979)

The paperback rights to author Richard Bach's slim allegory *Jonathan Livingston Seagull* go to Avon for a record $1.1 million (1972)

22

Alan Light

John Cleese

AUGUST 22, 1972
The Fool Monty
(Python, that is)

They unleashed their anarchic humour at home, a mix of outrageous skits and bits and graphics. For their stateside debut the Monty Python troupe stitched together some legs — no, wait, that was the Piranah Brothers. The Pythons stitched together favorites like the dead parrot sketch and the lumberjack song from the first two TV seasons into a film, *And Now For Something Completely Different*. Released today, it garnered good reviews but a meager audience unaccustomed to their atypical style. All that changed when PBS stations began airing the original BBC episodes a couple years later.

"A zany, irrepressible romp with wicked humor and cruel sideswipes... A cult show which, peddled correctly, could become a worldwide yockfest."

— VARIETY

Riding high as Mork, a bare-chested Robin Williams graces the cover of *Rolling Stone* as he discusses his feature film debut in Robert Altman's *Popeye* (1979)

23

Spinning off from *Diff'rent Strokes*, *The Facts of Life* opens a successful, often touching 9-year run on NBC (1979)

24

MOMA throws a 96th birthday party for John Bray, who released the first U.S. commercial cartoon, *The Dachshund and the Sausage*, in 1910 (1975)

25

Hard-rocking bar band Looking Glass hits #1 with an atypically mellow *Brandy (You're a Fine Girl)*, but the band soon disappears (1972)

26

The U.S. Open Tennis tournament bars transsexual Dr. Renee Richards from competing after she refuses to take a just-instituted chromosome test (1976)

27

Johnny Weismuller, Buster Crabbe, Jock Mahoney and James Pierce, former screen Tarzans all, commemorate the 100th anniversary of the birth of their character's creator, Edgar Rice Burroughs (1975)

28

29 One-hit wonders Mungo Jerry, a British skiffle quartet, rockets to #3 with the catchy *In the Summertime,* their only single to make the U.S. charts (1970)

30 Nobody discos down better than K.C. & the Sunshine Band with the #1 hit *Get Down Tonight,* the first of five boogying chart-topping singles (1975)

31 A mecca for independent film aficionados, the Telluride Film Festival, debuts (1974)

NOTES

Alan Light

AUGUST 30, 1974
Brady 'til Eternity

Wholesome, well-scrubbed kids + wise, tolerant parents = lots of gosh-o-golly good clean fun. *The Brady Bunch,* a throwback to '50s middle-class family sitcoms like *Ozzie & Harriet* and *Leave it to Beaver,* ended its 5-year run on ABC tonight. Never rating in the top 25 or winning any awards, it has nevertheless crossed the Rubicon to achieve elusive, enduring status as good ole Americana. Fans old and new show their undying loyalty in fresh Brady incarnations like sequels, specials, made-for-TV movies, theatricals and even a touring stage show.

"I still get so much fan mail addressed to Carol Brady, and I always answer, if it's legible."
—FLORENCE HENDERSON

September

1 Bobby Fischer becomes the first American to win the world chess title, defeating Boris Spassky of the USSR in Reykjavik, Iceland (1972)

2 Smuggling drugs in Turkey: a bad idea for young Brad Davis in *Midnight Express*, based on a true story with a script from Oliver Stone (1978)

3 John Lennon flies from Heathrow Airport to New York, marking the last time he'll ever set foot in England (1971)

4 Long before smash hits like *Silence of the Lambs* and *Philadelphia*, Jonathan Demme makes his directorial debut with a chick prison flick, *Caged Heat* (1974)

5 The world watches in horror after Arab terrorists invade the Israeli Olympic dorm in Munich, eventually resulting in the murder of 11 Israeli athletes (1972)

6 Derek & the Dominoes finish recording *Layla And Other Assorted Love Songs*; Eric Clapton's title track is inspired by his affair with Patty Boyd, then George Harrison's wife (1970), whom he later marries

7 Francois Truffaut's captivating film, *Day for Night*, debuts en route to the Oscar for best foreign film (1973)

iStockphoto

SEPTEMBER 7, 1979
Sports Action 24/7

As a former play-by-play broadcaster for the Hartford Whalers, Bill Rasmussen had a dream. He envisioned, along with his son Scott, a local sports network that would carry UConn games via satellite. But when he discovered that it would cost the same to transmit them nationally, that's just what he did. On this day he launched Entertainment & Sports Programming Network (later shortened to ESPN), buying an acre of land in an industrial park in Bristol, Connecticut for $9,000. Within a year Getty Oil recognized the potential and invested $100 million, and a heavyweight champion was born.

"The all-sports network format actually came to me in a traffic jam on I-84 in Hartford."

— BILL RASMUSSEN

September

SEPTEMBER 8, 1979
Occasionally Tacky Mackie

Versatile entertainer Carol Burnett ends her popular CBS variety show tonight. In its sketches she assumed many diverse personas, aided by a masterful off-screen hand: designer Bob Mackie. For the series' entire 11-year run he provided just the right clothes and accessories to enhance Burnett's winning characters. Next he shifts to over-the-top outlandishness for the bejeweled, bedazzling Cher, whose trademark look earns him nicknames like the sultan of sequins. Mackie's eclectic, star-studded clientele ranges from Marlene Dietrich to RuPaul, with even a dash of designer Barbie.

"We live in a jeans and tee-shirt world, but we all want to live in a palace."

—BOB MACKIE

See More Tales
and Tidbits at
www.365edge.com

8 Post-original series and pre-motion pictures, an animated *Star Trek,* with all of the cast members providing voices, debuts on NBC (1973)

9 Gilbert O'Sullivan's sad saga, *Alone Again Naturally,* again hits #1 after previously topping the charts in the summer, a rare return feat (1972)

10 A different brand of undercover cop: Paul Michael Glaser and David Soul make a freewheeling hip young duo in ABC's *Starsky & Hutch* (1975)

11 The sophomoric but successful spy spoof *Get Smart,* featuring Don Adams and Barbara Feldon, drops the cone of silence after a 5-year run (1970)

12 Sales of Jim Croce's *Time in a Bottle* take off when it's featured on an ABC movie, but the singer dies eight days later in a plane crash (1973)

13 A kinder, gentler detective series hits pay dirt as James Garner charms in Stephen Cannell's *The Rockford Files* (1974)

14 A manic Orkan (Robin Williams) propels *Mork and Mindy* to a smashing debut, but meddling producers soon mess up a good thing (1978)

15 Rumpled detective Peter Falk solves the murder (committed by a major guest star) that the audience sees opening every episode of *Columbo* (1971)

16 The doctor is in, the patients are out, way out, but nothing fazes the mild-mannered star of *The Bob Newhart Show* (1972)

17 A cast of catchy characters, all played by the popular comedian, make *The Flip Wilson Show* a hit and spawn a catchphrase: the Devil made me do it! (1970)

18 After leaving a message ("I need help bad, man") the night before on his manager's answering machine, Jimi Hendrix is found dead in his girlfriend's bed of a drug overdose in London (1970)

19 Mary, Mary, not contrary: a fresh figure — an unmarried, independent young woman — rises in *The Mary Tyler Moore Show* (1970)

20 In the highly hyped Battle of the Sexes, tennis champ Billie Jean King dusts off hustler Bobby Riggs in straight sets in the Astrodome (1973)

21 An institution, *Monday Night Football,* kicks off on ABC with Keith Jackson, dandy Don Meredith and the voluble Howard Cosell (1970)

M*A*S*H

SEPTEMBER 17, 1972
Momentous *M*A*S*H*

Many movies spawn pale TV series that quickly disappear. Tonight that rarest of confluent entertainment dawns: *M*A*S*H,* a spinoff sitcom that not only equals but in many ways eclipses the popular Robert Altman film. The black comedy runs for 11 years — nearly four times longer than the conflict it depicted, the Korean War — and provides a tart, topical correlation to the then raging Vietnam War. Alan Alda, the only cast member to appear in every episode, wins Emmys for acting, writing and directing — the only actor to do so on one series. Its 2-1/2-hour finale in 1983 captures 105.9 million viewers, making it the most-watched TV show of all time.

"I'll carry your books, I'll carry a torch, I'll carry a tune, I'll carry on, carry over, carry forward, Cary Grant, cash and carry, carry me back to Old Virginia. I'll even hari-kari if you show me how, but I will not carry a gun!"

— HAWKEYE PIERCE
(ALAN ALDA)

SEPTEMBER 22, 1976
Jiggle TV

The more the critics carped ("massage parlor television"), the more the public tuned in. *Charlie's Angels* debuted tonight to a big audience and soon its sexy, shapely trio—Kate Jackson, Jaclyn Smith and Farrah Fawcett-Majors—were major stars. Especially Farrah, whose pinup poster became all the rage. Unseen John Forsythe provided the melodious voice of the mysterious Charlie, but the real man responsible for this show and lots more was producer Aaron Spelling, Tori's papa. His prolific run of young-skewing ABC hits (*Mod Squad, The Love Boat* & lots more) led to a snickering network nickname: "Aaron's Broadcasting Company."

"Stay tuned—I may not be here, but my show was picked up!"

— AARON SPELLING

---

22 The King stands alone: a rare *Rolling Stone* cover with no multiple story teases, just a handsome head shot labeled "Elvis Presley, 1935-1977" (1977)

23 British glam rockers Mott the Hoople release their biggest single, *All the Young Dudes,* penned by David Bowie (1972)

24 The novel took six days but the movie halves it in the harrowing *Three Days of the Condor,* with a dynamic Redford/Dunaway pairing (1975)

25 *The Partridge Family* debuts, and within a month *I Think I Love You* tops the pop charts and launches the career of teen idol David Cassidy (1970)

26 *Sports Illustrated* prevails in a lawsuit, so female reporters are now allowed locker room access after baseball games (1978)

27 The hard-rockin' Wilson sisters, Ann and Nancy, of Heart score their first top ten single, *Magic Man* (1976)

28 Glam rocker David Bowie and his band, the Spiders, go through some ch-changes as they sell out Carnegie Hall, their first ever NYC concert (1972)

September

29 Riding hits like *Peace Train* and *Morning Has Broken,* Cat Stevens begins a 31-date North American tour with a sold-out show at the Shrine Auditorium in L.A. (1972)

30 The sultry, long-lived actress who shot to stardom opposite Bogart in *To Have and Have Not* tells all in her first autobiography, *Lauren Bacall, By Myself* (1979)

NOTES

iStockphoto

SEPTEMBER 1977
Gourmet Grocery

Little corner groceries helped feed countless generations of city dwellers before the advent of supermarket chains. Today a former cheese shop owner and his partner take a page out of history by opening Dean and Deluca in New York. The space's high, white walls with ceiling fans spinning above evoke a turn-of-the-century grocery. But the main attraction is its ambitious array of delectable foodstuffs plus quality kitchen accessories. It soon becomes a New York destination that presages the natural food offerings of chains like Whole Foods, which begins three years later. Meanwhile, on the upper East Side, another food feast debuts: Smith and Wollenksy, the steak house supreme.

"SoHo, ever burgeoning with art galleries, boutiques and restaurants has an addition in the area of 'gourmandise.' "

— AN EARLY
  NEWSPAPER
  REVIEW

October

October

1 The Magic Kingdom (a.k.a. Disney World) opens in Florida (1971)

2 Two-time winner: Rod Stewart's single *Maggie May* and album *Every Picture Tells A Story* simultaneously hit #1 (1971)

3 A black & white snapshot of small town life emerges in *The Last Picture Show*, adapted from a Larry McMurtry novel (1971)

4 In Hollywood to record the album *Pearl,* Janis Joplin, 27, is found dead of a heroin overdose at the Franklin Motel (1970)

5 Bo Derek's a perfect *10,* with besotted Dudley Moore rating her an eleven (1979)

6 Is it safe? A sadistic Nazi dentist (Laurence Olivier) seeks a cache of diamonds stashed in New York, with Dustin Hoffman in the way, in the taut thriller *Marathon Man* (1976)

7 George Burns plays the Almighty and John Denver's his messenger in Carl Reiner's loveable *Oh, God!* (1977)

Library of Congress: N.Y. World-Telegram & Sun Collection

OCTOBER 7, 1971
Popeye the Cop

The French Connection roars onscreen this day with one of film's most riveting chase sequences ever. Everyman cop "Popeye" Doyle (Gene Hackman) races in a car underneath an elevated subway line down 86th Street to catch a drug hit man. When director William Friedkin first approaches NYC authorities, they deny permission for such a dangerous, unprecedented stunt. But one powerful transit boss makes him an offer: $40,000 and a one-way ticket to Jamaica. Friedkin gives it to him and gets the scene. The boss gets fired, as he'd expected, and the movie goes on to win five Oscars including best picture, director and editing.

"The son of a bitch is here. I saw him. I'm gonna get him."

—DOYLE (GENE HACKMAN), SEARCHING FOR A DRUG KINGPIN (FERNANDO REY) WHO ESCAPES IN THE MOVIE, AND IN REAL LIFE

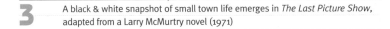

Dan Aykroyd

NATPE

OCTOBER 11, 1972
Saturday Night's Alright For Programming

When Johnny Carson asked that his weekend reruns (*Best of Carson*) move to weeknights so he could take more time off, NBC cast about for something new. It tapped Canadian producer Lorne Michaels to design a young sketch/musical/variety show, and voila — *NBC's Saturday Night* (later *Saturday Night Live*) debuted this night with host George Carlin. And so kicked off an institution with an edgy blend of satire, star hosts and musical guests, and a resident troupe (the Not Yet Ready For Prime-Time Players) of breakout talent: Chevy Chase, John Belushi, Dan Aykroyd, Gilda Radner, Garrett Morris, Jane Curtin and Laraine Newman in year one alone.

"It's better when they laugh, isn't it?"

—LORNE MICHAELS

Don Cornelius's *Soul Train* embarks on a long syndicated run featuring R&B, soul, hip-hop with an occasional touch of gospel or jazz (1971)

8

A Jethro Tull concert at Madison Square Garden is beamed live via satellite to an estimated worldwide audience of 400 million (1978)

9

First the King (see Dec. 21st), now the Godfather: soul showman James Brown visits the White House to chat up President Nixon (1972)

10

Great gosh almighty: the Pointer Sisters smooth debut single *Yes We Can Can* peaks at #11 (1973)

11

Andrew Lloyd Webber's controversial rock opera *Jesus Christ Superstar* opens on Broadway with a smashing soundtrack, and a movie looms (1971)

12

A plane crash in the Andes forces surviving rugby teammates to take desperate measures (1972); inspires the 1993 movie *Alive!* with Ethan Hawke and Vincent Spano

13

Grassy plains grasshopper: David Carradine roams the old west, doling out a unique form of frontier justice in *Kung Fu* (1972)

14

15 Madison Square Garden fans boo Rick Nelson for trying new material, motivating him to write *Garden Party,* his first top ten hit in nearly a decade (1971)

16 Get in line: gasoline shortages disrupt America when the Arab-dominated OPEC cuts the normal flow of oil to the U.S. (1973)

17 Prolific rock guitarist Eric Clapton lets it all hang out in *After Midnight,* his first solo single (1970)

18 Calamity plane: *Airport 1975,* one of the popular aerial disaster flicks opens with Karen ("the stewardess is flying the plane!") Black (1975)

19 The U.S. Postal Service pulls a poster commemorating the 50th anniversary of talking pictures due to its portrayal of Al Jolson in blackface in the *Jazz Singer* (1977)

20 President Jimmy Carter leads a crowd of 6,000 at the dedication of the John F. Kennedy Library in Boston (1979)

21 Despite having come close with *School Day* (#3) and *Sweet Little Sixteen* (#2), Chuck Berry doesn't hit #1 until today with the rude *My Ding-A-Ling* (1972)

Library of Congress: N.Y. World-Telegram & Sun Collection

OCTOBER 18, 1972
Lady Blue

The critics had a field day. Diana Ross as jazz icon Billie Holiday — who does she think she is? But the breakout star from the Supremes, who'd departed the group two years before for a solo career, changed a lot of minds when *Lady Sings the Blues* debuted in New York. Her performance won rave reviews and Golden Globe (which she won) and Oscar nominations. Also debuting in the film was Richard Pryor as the piano man, while Billy Dee Williams played her lover – a pairing so successful that they reprised it two years later in the inferior *Mahogany*, though each film did generate successful soundtrack albums.

"You got a long way to go before anybody gonna pay $2 for an hour of your time."

—A MADAM (ISABEL SANFORD)
TO BILLIE HOLIDAY

Alan Light

OCTOBER 25, 1978
A Slash Smash

Shooting in three weeks with an unknown lead actress and a micro budget of $325,000, the film wasn't expected to have much of an impact. But that lead, Jamie Lee Curtis, had famous parentage — particularly her mother, Janet Leigh, known forever for her shower scream scene in Alfred Hitchcock's *Psycho*. Borrowing liberally from that and other horror classics, the savvily promoted *Halloween* torched the box office for $47 million. And so was born the horny teenage slasher movie genre, spawning an often horrid horde of imitative franchises like *Friday the 13th* and *Nightmare on Elm Street*. Beware of things that go slash in the night.

" 'Halloween' is an absolutely merciless thriller, a movie so violent and scary that, yes, I would compare it to 'Psycho.' "

— ROGER EBERT

22 Rock me two times: both sides of Queen's 45, *We Are The Champions* and *We Will Rock You*, get extensive airplay en route to #4 (1977)

23 Implicated in the death of his roadie turned companion Nancy Spungin, Sid Vicious attempts suicide in a NYC jail; the Sex Pistols bassist dies from a heroin OD several months later (1978)

24 Who loves ya, baby? Telly Savalas becomes a TV star as a gruff tough (on the outside) NYC detective in *Kojak* (1973)

25 Playwright Neil Simon weds actress Marsha Mason, three weeks after they met on the set of *The Good Doctor* (1973)

26 *Bull Tales*, Garry Trudeau's cartoon strip from the *Yale Daily News*, makes its debut as a nationally syndicated strip under a new name, *Doonesbury* (1970)

27 A generational clash erupts between father (Robert Duvall) and son (Miles O'Keefe) in *The Great Santini*, adapted from Pat Conroy's bestseller (1979)

28 He's kinda dangerous: Nick Gilder tops the charts with his suggestive, slinky *Hot Child in The City* (1978)

29 Duane Allman dies in a motorcycle accident in Macon, Georgia (1971); one year later Allman Brothers bassist Berry Oakley does the same on his chopper three blocks away

30 In Plymouth, Massachusetts, Bob Dylan kicks off his Rolling Thunder Revue with an eclectic mix of talent including Joan Baez, Bowie guitarist Mick Ronson, *Nashville* star Ronee Blakley and poet Allen Ginsberg (1975)

31 NBC's first *Dean Martin Celebrity Roast* of Bob Hope features guests from Neil Armstrong to John Wayne and future roastees Telly Savalas and Mr. T (1974)

NOTES

OCTOBER 30, 1971
Imagine A Better Place

An instant hit, a classic, a plea for peace — John Lennon's *Imagine* is simultaneously all these. Subsequently, sadly, this signature tune will also become an epitaph, but today it's all aces as the album reigns at #1 in both the U.S. and U.K. Lennon dislikes the added syrupy strings, describing the sound as "chocolate coated," but the album clicks with fans even more than his successful first solo effort, *John Lennon/Plastic Ono Band* (let's forget Yoko's screechy companion album, shall we?). But it's not all sweetness and light: *Imagine* also contains two thinly veiled attacks on former partner Paul, *How Do You Sleep?* and *Crippled Inside.*

"God is a concept by which we measure our pain."

— JOHN LENNON

November

1 Hal Holbrook and Martin Sheen co-star in ABC's *That Certain Summer,* one of the earliest sympathetic TV portrayals of homosexuality (1972)

2 Crosby, Stills, Nash and Young have come *So Far*: #1 on the album charts for their anthology featuring recognized tunes like *Ohio, Déjà Vu* and *Teach Your Children* (1974)

3 Musical hookup: Carly Simon weds James Taylor in her NYC apartment (1972), a marriage that'll last ten years and produce two children

4 Bad dreams come true: ostracized Sissy Spacek makes her mean high school classmates pay in Brian De Palma's bloody horror classic, *Carrie* (1976)

5 A group of right-wing anti-Marxist youths wreck a Madrid art gallery and destroy 24 engravings by Pablo Picasso (1971)

6 Cher, minus Sonny, scores her first #1 hit with *Gypsys, Tramps & Thieves* (1971)

7 More than three decades after its Oscar-winning debut, *Gone With the Wind* makes its TV premiere over two nights on NBC (1976)

iStockphoto

NOVEMBER 1971
Punk High Priestess

Former schoolteacher turned seamstress Vivienne Westwood, along with her provocateur partner Malcolm McLaren, open Let It Rock at 430 King's Road in London. At first catering to the '50s revival, "Teddy Boy" subculture, the shop next becomes Too Fast to Live, Too Young to Die. That incarnation focuses on the Brando-influenced, biker/rocker style. In 1974 these shrewd entrepreneurs change the name to Sex, and its ragged mix of S&M-inspired leather, chains, zippers, ripped clothing and pornographic tee shirts define and launch the punk look. It becomes the epicenter of the punk fashion scene, the place where the future Sex Pistols meet.

"Even though it was the 70s, we found old stocks of clothes that had never been worn from the 50s and took them apart. I started to teach myself how to make clothes from that kind of formula."

—VIVIENNE WESTWOOD

Library of Congress: N.Y. World-Telegram & Sun Collection

NOVEMBER 8, 1972
A Great Notion

In its early days, cable television systems delivered existing broadcast signals into rural homes. Solving poor on-air reception was its only selling point. Pioneer Chuck Dolan envisioned another: a pay channel with fresh programming. Today, Home Box Office premiered via terrestrial microwave to a few hundred homes in Wilkes-Barre, Pennsylvania with an NHL game from Madison Square Garden and the prophetically titled movie *Sometimes a Great Notion,* directed by and starring Paul Newman. Media giant Time soon acquired the fledgling network, while Dolan went on to build his own cable system and programming (Bravo, AMC) empire.

"For the first ten years, we didn't sell cable TV – we sold HBO."

— CABLE PIONEER
  JOHN MALONE

See More Tales
and Tidbits at
www.365edge.com

Tom Dempsey of the N.O. Saints kicks a record 63-yard field goal in a 19-17 win over the Detroit Lions (1970)

8

Cat Stevens makes his U.S. television debut on ABC's *In Concert* at the Hollywood Bowl (1973), but by decade's end he'll abandon pop to become a devout Muslim

9

Man vs. Machine: Steven Spielberg makes his directorial debut with a TV movie about a panicked, pursued businessman (Dennis Weaver) in *Duel* (1971)

10

Ten years after actor Richard Harris reached #2, Donna Summer's disco-fied version of *MacArthur Park* hits #1 (1978)

11

Hip-hop debuts when a former gang member, renamed Afrika Bambaataa, forms the Universal Zulu Nation in NYC (1973)

12

En route to meet union officials and a newspaper reporter, Karen Silkwood, a critic of nuclear plant safety procedures, dies in a mysterious automobile accident (1974), later dramatized in *Silkwood* starring Meryl Streep

13

A throwback to TV's golden age, a star-laden remake of *All Quiet on the Western Front,* is directed by Delbert Mann and features Ernest Borgnine, Patricia Neal and Ian Holm (1979)

14

15 Linda Lovelace stars in *Deep Throat,* which along with *Behind the Green Door* ushers in a brief period of porno chic (1972)

16 Five years before *E.T.,* Steven Spielberg explores interplanetary interconnections with *Close Encounters of the Third Kind* (1977)

17 The first of a half-dozen Olivia Newton-John TV specials features an eclectic guest list from Rona Barrett to Rock Hudson (1976)

18 President Nixon signs legislation making it illegal to shoot or hunt birds, fish or other animals from an airplane (1971)

19 Inspired asylum antics in Milos Forman's *One Flew Over the Cuckoo's Nest* leads to a sweep of all five top Oscars: picture, director, lead actor and actress, and screenplay (1975)

20 Once hoping to play the film's lead, Isaac Hayes turns his assignment — writing its music — into a memorable #1 hit with the theme from *Shaft* (1971)

21 The Muppets do disco as *Sesame Street Fever,* with a little help from Robin Gibb, goes gold (500,000 units) (1978)

Michael Reeve

NOVEMBER 17, 1976
Golden Child

The ancient boy-king Tutankhamun may have been dead for centuries, but he can still attract a crowd. His tomb, first discovered by Egyptologist Howard Carter in 1922, made King Tut an instant celebrity. Today, lines wrap around the National Gallery of Art as *Treasures of Tutankhamun* opens in Washington, D.C. The 55 objects on display from his tomb include his solid gold funeral mask, a gilded wood figure of the goddess Selket, lamps, jars, jewelry and furniture. More than 800,000 visitors attend the 4-month exhibition, and over the next four years the traveling show attracts some eight million visitors in the U.S. alone.

"As my eyes grew accustomed to the light, details of the room within emerged slowly from the mist, strange animals, statues and gold — everywhere the glint of gold."

—EXPLORER HOWARD CARTER

Markadet

NOVEMBER 25, 1971
Fear & Loathing

Destruction. Degradation. Drugs. Embodying the new term "gonzo journalism" (coined by a friend), Hunter S. Thompson explodes onto the literary scene with *Fear & Loathing in Las Vegas: A Savage Trip to the Heart of the American Dream,* of which *Rolling Stone* publishes the second part today. The "scorching epochal sensation" (Tom Wolfe) follows the drug-fueled exploits of journalist Raoul Duke and his 300-pound Samoan attorney, Dr. Gonzo, in and around a narcotics officers' convention. Featuring equally crazed, brilliant artwork by Ralph Stedman, it catapults Thompson to fame, more fear, and fiction (Duke in *Doonesbury*).

"A word to the wise is infuriating."
—HUNTER S. THOMPSON

22 Sony premieres its first Betamax product, a combination TV/VCR listing for $2,295, but the company eventually loses the video format war to VHS (1975)

23 The FDA proposes warning labels be affixed to aerosol sprays stating that fluorocarbons may harm the environment by reducing the ozone layer (1976)

24 Ingrid Bergman wins an Oscar in a star-studded adaptation of Agatha Christie's famed whodunit, *Murder on the Orient Express* (1974)

25 Don McLean's musical paean, *American Pie,* clocking in at 8 minutes, 22 seconds, debuts en route to #1 and eternal anthem status (1971)

26 ABC premieres an *All-Star Tribute to John Wayne* with host Frank Sinatra and guests Charles Bronson, Angie Dickinson, Ron Howard and Lee Marvin (1976)

27 The movies gleefully skewer television in Sidney Lumet's manic *Network,* which wins four Oscars including a posthumous one for Peter Finch (1976)

28 John Lennon joins Elton John onstage at Madison Square Garden where they perform three tunes including *Whatever Gets You Through the Night* (1974)

29   Fred Silverman makes TV history when he cancels all seven of his predecessor's new series, about a third of last place NBC's primetime lineup (1978)

30   Cashing in: Kenny Rogers' *The Gambler* — a Grammy winner and his signature song — goes gold (500,000 units) (1978)

Library of Congress; N.Y. World-Telegram & Sun Collection

A. Homicz

NOVEMBER 30, 1977
David & Crosby

Crooner Bing Crosby began his beloved Christmas specials on radio in 1936, and later segued to television. Mixing in lots of high-profile guests, from Maurice Chevalier to old pal Bob Hope, he often included more contemporary acts to attract the younger set. So in 1977, with the enthusiastic support of his kids, he chose David Bowie, whom he previously knew nothing about. The two met in London in September when Bing was on tour and recorded duets on *Peace on Earth* and *Little Drummer Boy.* Bing died a month later, and the special debuted on this day.

CROSBY: *Do you go in for any of the traditional things at Christmastime?*

BOWIE: *Oh yeah, most of them really. Presents, tree, decorations, agents sliding down the chimney...*

CROSBY: *What??*

BOWIE: *Oh, I was just seeing if you were paying attention.*

Markadet

NOVEMBER 25, 1971
Fear & Loathing

Destruction. Degradation. Drugs. Embodying the new term "gonzo journalism" (coined by a friend), Hunter S. Thompson explodes onto the literary scene with *Fear & Loathing in Las Vegas: A Savage Trip to the Heart of the American Dream,* of which *Rolling Stone* publishes the second part today. The "scorching epochal sensation" (Tom Wolfe) follows the drug-fueled exploits of journalist Raoul Duke and his 300-pound Samoan attorney, Dr. Gonzo, in and around a narcotics officers' convention. Featuring equally crazed, brilliant artwork by Ralph Stedman, it catapults Thompson to fame, more fear, and fiction (Duke in *Doonesbury*).

"A word to the wise is infuriating."
—HUNTER S. THOMPSON

22 Sony premieres its first Betamax product, a combination TV/VCR listing for $2,295, but the company eventually loses the video format war to VHS (1975)

23 The FDA proposes warning labels be affixed to aerosol sprays stating that fluorocarbons may harm the environment by reducing the ozone layer (1976)

24 Ingrid Bergman wins an Oscar in a star-studded adaptation of Agatha Christie's famed whodunit, *Murder on the Orient Express* (1974)

25 Don McLean's musical paean, *American Pie,* clocking in at 8 minutes, 22 seconds, debuts en route to #1 and eternal anthem status (1971)

26 ABC premieres an *All-Star Tribute to John Wayne* with host Frank Sinatra and guests Charles Bronson, Angie Dickinson, Ron Howard and Lee Marvin (1976)

27 The movies gleefully skewer television in Sidney Lumet's manic *Network,* which wins four Oscars including a posthumous one for Peter Finch (1976)

28 John Lennon joins Elton John onstage at Madison Square Garden where they perform three tunes including *Whatever Gets You Through the Night* (1974)

29 Fred Silverman makes TV history when he cancels all seven of his predecessor's new series, about a third of last place NBC's primetime lineup (1978)

30 Cashing in: Kenny Rogers' *The Gambler* — a Grammy winner and his signature song — goes gold (500,000 units) (1978)

Library of Congress: N.Y. World-Telegram & Sun Collection

NOVEMBER 30, 1977
David & Crosby

Crooner Bing Crosby began his beloved Christmas specials on radio in 1936, and later segued to television. Mixing in lots of high-profile guests, from Maurice Chevalier to old pal Bob Hope, he often included more contemporary acts to attract the younger set. So in 1977, with the enthusiastic support of his kids, he chose David Bowie, whom he previously knew nothing about. The two met in London in September when Bing was on tour and recorded duets on *Peace on Earth* and *Little Drummer Boy.* Bing died a month later, and the special debuted on this day.

CROSBY: *Do you go in for any of the traditional things at Christmastime?*

BOWIE: *Oh yeah, most of them really. Presents, tree, decorations, agents sliding down the chimney...*

CROSBY: *What??*

BOWIE: *Oh, I was just seeing if you were paying attention.*

A. Homicz

December

1 *Mademoiselle* lists 18 men with "Movie Machismo" including Brando, Pacino, Raul Julia, Jon Voight, Mark Spitz and (?) Woody Allen (1972)

2 Speculation abounds over Carly Simon's future #1, *You're So Vain,* released today: is it about backup vocalist Mick Jagger, Kris Kristofferson or (our choice) Warren Beatty? (1972)

3 Richard Pryor and Gene Wilder make a disorderly comedic duo in the cross-country adventure, *Silver Streak* (1976)

4 *Mommie Dearest,* Christina Crawford's scathing tell-all book about her famous actress mother, Joan Crawford, tops the bestseller list (1978)

5 Featuring a searing cover of Donovan's *Season of the Witch,* the album *Super Session* with Mike Bloomfield, Al Kooper and Stephen Stills, goes gold (500,000 units) (1970)

6 Ten years after NBC cancelled the initial series, *Star Trek: The Motion Picture* hits the big screen and regenerates Trek-mania (1979)

7 Cashing in on a martial arts craze, Carl Douglas hits #1 with *Kung Fu Fighting* while another one-hit wonder, Carol Douglas, makes #11 with *Doctor's Orders* (1974)

DECEMBER 3, 1971
Outspoken. Outrageous. Outstanding.

Idiosyncratic avant-garde artist Frank Zappa attracted a devoted cult following whilst confounding the masses. Tonight when his band, The Mothers of Invention, played the Montreux Casino in Switzerland, a fan fired a flare that set the roof ablaze. The joint burned down, and though no one was hurt the band lost $50,000 of equipment. Deep Purple, recording nearby, appropriated the event for their hit *Smoke On the Water.* Zappa's bad luck continued a week later when the jealous boyfriend of an ardent female fan pushed him offstage, breaking his leg and ankle and fracturing his skull. After he died in 1993, fans in Vilnius, Lithuania had this bust (above) erected.

"Phi Zappa Krappa."

—A FAMOUS B&W POSTER OF ZAPPA SITTING ON THE TOILET

December

Library of Congress: N.Y. World-Telegram & Sun Collection

DECEMBER 8, 1972
And the Colored Girls Sing

Having quit NYC's talented but fractious Velvet Underground several years earlier, Lou Reed transforms his world today with the release of his gender-bending album *Transformer*. Co-produced in London by David Bowie, the seminal glam rock release features the dirty ditty *Walk on the Wild Side* that's edited and/or banned in several countries. It's one of several tracks influenced or suggested by Andy Warhol and his bohemian coterie. Reed's next album, the gloomy *Berlin*, features Stevie Winwood and Jack Druce among others.

"A hustle here and a hustle there, New York City's the place where they say, hey babe, take a walk on the wild side."

—LOU REED

See More Tales
and Tidbits at
www.365edge.com

Michael Cimino's *The Deer Hunter* opens, packing an emotional antiwar wallop en route to five Oscars including best picture and director (1978)

8

Helen Reddy's *I Am Woman* hits #1, and when accepting a Grammy she enrages fundamentalists by thanking God for her success "because She makes everything possible" (1972)

9

Gamesmanship galore when two veterans, Michael Caine and Laurence Olivier, match mysterious moves in *Sleuth* (1972)

10

Bob Seger and the Silver Bullet Band release *Night Moves*, their first top ten hit (1976)

11

A career sailor (Jack Nicholson) leads *The Last Detail*, helming the transport of a hapless prisoner (Randy Quaid) to the brig with some detours (1973)

12

In the midst of a 30-date tour, George Harrison stops by the White House while in Washington, D.C. and has a nice chat with President Ford (1974)

13

Whistle-blowing NYC cop Frank Serpico testifies about police corruption (1971), and his story later becomes a feature film starring Al Pacino

14

15 Christopher Reeve soars onscreen in a dynamic, big-budget *Superman* with a host of supporting players from Brando to Susannah York (1978)

16 Based on a magazine story later exposed as fiction, *Saturday Night Fever* nevertheless launches, boogies into disco history — and dictates questionable fashion (1977)

17 Entrepreneurial Ted Turner beams his small UHF Atlanta station nationwide via a satellite slot and launches Superstation WTBS (1976)

18 The debut of back-to-back #1 hits for the Eagles: *New Kid in Town* and the ethereal, eternal *Hotel California* (1976)

19 Two top films open on the same day: Peter Sellers' *Being There* and the Meryl Streep/Dustin Hoffman family drama *Kramer vs. Kramer* (1979)

20 The sweet sleeper *Harold and Maude* opens, with generationally challenged Bud Cort and Ruth Gordon making a most unusual couple (1971)

21 Elvis is in the (White) House: a fawning note penned by Elvis Presley nets him a meeting with President Nixon (1970)

DECEMBER 19, 1971
Rebellion and Rebirth

Scathing satire and ritualistic violence so extreme that the publication of Anthony Burgess's novel introduced a new catchword, "ultraviolence." Stanley Kubrick's film version of *A Clockwork Orange* explodes onscreen today and immediately triggers controversy and condemnation. Set in a bleak futuristic world, it catapults mesmerizing lead Malcolm McDowell to stardom. Kubrick cuts thirty seconds to achieve an "R" instead of "X" rating, but later approves the film's ban in England after several real-life copycat assaults that mimicked the attacks of Alex (McDowell) and his "droogs" (mates).

"It was a bit from the Glorious Ninth by Ludwig Van."

—ALEX (MALCOLM MCDOWELL), REFERRING TO HIS FAVORITE PIECE OF MUSIC BESIDES *SINGIN' IN THE RAIN*

December

iStockphoto

DECEMBER 26, 1973
The Devil Made Her Do It

Demonic possession, a popular box-office theme, had made a hit out of *Rosemary's Baby*. Today came an even more sensational and shocking horror tale, *The Exorcist*. Voted the scariest movie ever by *Entertainment Weekly*, this adaptation of a William Blatty novel by director William Friedkin (coming off *The French Connection*) featured a head-turning, stomach-churning debut by Linda Blair as the young girl possessed by Satan. It caused such a commotion — audience hysteria and fainting and such — that the studio provided free barf bags. Its overdubbed instrumental theme, *Tubular Bells*, later became a top ten hit for Mike Oldfield.

"You're telling me that I should take my daughter to a witch doctor, is that it?"

—CHRIS MACNEIL
(ELLEN BURSTYN)

22 Do you feel lucky, punk? Iconoclastic cop Clink Eastwood prowls the alleys and streets of San Francisco in search of a serial killer in *Dirty Harry* (1971)

23 Rod Stewart, who'll perform *Do Ya Think I'm Sexy* at an upcoming U.N. benefit concert, announces that he'll donate all royalties from the song to UNICEF (1978)

24 James Taylor, Carly Simon, Linda Ronstadt and Joni Mitchell sing Christmas carols on the streets of L.A. (1974)

25 The con is on: Newman and Redford reunite in *The Sting*, a rollicking yarn that goes on to win seven Oscars including best picture and director (1973)

26 Long past his hit-making prime 'til last year's surprise #1, *Too Much, Too Little, Too Late* with Deniece Williams, crooner Johnny Mathis catches holiday cheer when his album *Give Me Your Love For Christmas* goes gold (500,000 units) (1979)

27 Eclectic English rockers Roxy Music, led by Brian Ferry, debut their biggest single to date, the catchy dance number *Love is the Drug* (1975)

28 Doo woppers Sha Na Na play Carnegie Hall in NYC, and the Who's Keith Moon serves as emcee (1971)

29 Life as we knew it: after 36 years as the nation's leading weekly, *Life* magazine publishes its last weekly issue (1972)

30 Wild things for the holidays as Maurice Sendak's classic kid's characters decorate a monster Christmas tree on the cover of *Rolling Stone* (1976)

31 The eternally youthful host, replacing earlier generational icon Guy Lombardo, debuts *Dick Clark's New Year's Rockin' Eve* on ABC (1972)

NOTES

U.S. National Archives

DECEMBER 28, 1978
Aristocratic Art

The infamous political, partisan bickering of Washington, D.C. ceases, at least for one evening, as entertainment's most legendary and luminous figures arrive at the Kennedy Center. Welcome to the grand opening of the Kennedy Center Honors, telecast tonight on CBS. The celebration honors five inductees — Marian Anderson, Fred Astaire, George Balanchine, Richard Rodgers and Arthur Rubinstein — for "their lifetime contributions to American culture through the performing arts, whether in dance, music, theater, opera, motion pictures or television." England bestows knighthood, France has the Legion of Honor, and now America has national recognition for excellence in the arts. Bravo.

"I look forward to an America which will not be afraid of grace and beauty... which will award achievement in the arts as we award achievement in business or statecraft."

—PRESIDENT JOHN F. KENNEDY, FROM A SPEECH WHEN THE CENTER WAS FIRST PROPOSED

Books

August, 1914 Alexander Solzhenitsyn

Breakfast of Champions Kurt Vonnegut

Centennial James A. Michener

Chesapeake James A. Michener

Curtain Agatha Christie

Dolores Jacqueline Susann

The Exorcist William P. Blatty

Fools Die Mario Puzo

The French Lieutenant's Woman John Fowles

Illusions: The Adventures of a Reluctant Messiah Richard Bach

Islands in the Stream Ernest Hemingway

Jaws Peter Benchley

Jonathan Livingston Seagull Richard Bach

Love Story Erich Segal

The Matarese Circle Robert Ludlum

The Moneychangers Arthur Hailey

The Odessa File Frederick Forsyth

Once Is Not Enough Jacqueline Susann

Overload Arthur Hailey

The Passions of the Mind Irving Stone

Ragtime E. L. Doctorow

The Silmarillion J.R.R. Tolkien and Christopher Tolkien

Sleeping Murder Agatha Christie

Sophie's Choice William Styron

The Thorn Birds Colleen McCullough

Tinker, Tailor, Soldier, Spy John Le Carré

Trinity Leon Uris

War and Remembrance Herman Wouk

Watership Down Richard Adams

Wheels Arthur Hailey

Movies

1970   Picture: *Patton*

Actor: **George C. Scott** (*Patton*)

Actress: **Glenda Jackson** (*Women in Love*)

Supporting Actor: **John Mills** (*Ryan's Daughter*)

Supporting Actress: **Helen Hayes** (*Airport*)

Director: **Franklin Schaffner** (*Patton*)

1971   Picture: *The French Connection*

Actor: **Gene Hackman** (*The French Connection*)

Actress: **Jane Fonda** (*Klute*)

Supporting Actor: **Ben Johnson** (*The Last Picture Show*)

Supporting Actress: **Cloris Leachman** (*The Last Picture Show*)

Director: **William Friedkin** (*The French Connection*)

1972   Picture: *The Godfather*

Actor: **Marlon Brando** (*The Godfather*)

Actress: **Liza Minnelli** (*Cabaret*)

Supporting Actor: **Joel Grey** (*Cabaret*)

Supporting Actress: **Eileen Heckart** (*Butterflies Are Free*)

Director: **Bob Fosse** (*Cabaret*)

1973   Picture: *The Sting*

Actor: **Jack Lemmon** (*Save the Tiger*)

Actress: **Glenda Jackson** (*A Touch of Class*)

Supporting Actor: **John Houseman** (*The Paper Chase*)

Supporting Actress: **Tatum O'Neal** (*Paper Moon*)

Director: **George Roy Hill** (*The Sting*)

1974   Picture: *The Godfather, Part II*

Actor: **Art Carney** (*Harry & Tonto*)

Actress: **Ellen Burstyn** (*Alice Doesn't Live Here Anymore*)

Supporting Actor: **Robert De Niro** (*The Godfather, Part II*)

Supporting Actress: **Ingrid Bergman** (*Murder on the Orient Express*)

Director: **Francis Ford Coppola** (*The Godfather, Part II*)

Movies

1975 Picture: *One Flew Over the Cuckoo's Nest*
Actor: **Jack Nicholson** (*One Flew Over the Cuckoo's Nest*)
Actress: **Louise Fletcher** (*One Flew Over the Cuckoo's Nest*)
Supporting Actor: **George Burns** (*The Sunshine Boys*)
Supporting Actress: **Lee Grant** (*Shampoo*)
Director: **Milos Forman** (*One Flew Over the Cuckoo's Nest*)

1976 Picture: *Rocky*
Actor: **Peter Finch** (*Network*)
Actress: **Faye Dunaway** (*Network*)
Supporting Actor: **Jason Robards** (*All the President's Men*)
Supporting Actress: **Beatrice Straight** (*Network*)
Director: **John Avildsen** (*Rocky*)

1977 Picture: *Annie Hall*
Actor: **Richard Dreyfuss** (*The Goodbye Girl*)
Actress: **Diane Keaton** (*Annie Hall*)
Supporting Actor: **Jason Robards** (*Julia*)
Supporting Actress: **Vanessa Redgrave** (*Julia*)
Director: **Woody Allen** (*Annie Hall*)

1978 Picture: *The Deer Hunter*
Actor: **Jon Voight** (*Coming Home*)
Actress: **Jane Fonda** (*Coming Home*)
Supporting Actor: **Christopher Walken** (*The Deer Hunter*)
Supporting Actress: **Maggie Smith** (*California Suite*)
Director: **Michael Cimino** (*The Deer Hunter*)

1979 Picture: *Kramer vs. Kramer*
Actor: **Dustin Hoffman** (*Kramer vs. Kramer*)
Actress: **Sally Field** (*Norma Rae*)
Supporting Actor: **Melvyn Douglas** (*Being There*)
Supporting Actress: **Meryl Streep** (*Kramer vs. Kramer*)
Director: **Robert Benton** (*Kramer vs. Kramer*)

the **70**s

Movies

The Top 25 Movies of the 1970s

Airport

American Graffiti

Blazing Saddles

Close Encounters of the Third Kind

Every Which Way But Loose

The Exorcist

The Godfather

Grease

Jaws

Jaws 2

Kramer vs. Kramer

Love Story

*M*A*S*H*

National Lampoon's Animal House

One Flew Over the Cuckoo's Nest

Patton

The Poseidon Adventure

Rocky

Smokey and the Bandit

Star Wars

The Sting

Summer of '42

Superman

The Towering Inferno

Young Frankenstein

The Top 25 Television Shows of the 1970s

60 Minutes
Alice
All in the Family
The Bionic Woman
Bridget Loves Bernie
Charlie's Angels
Chico and The Man
The Flip Wilson Show
Gunsmoke
Happy Days
Hawaii Five-O
Here's Lucy
Ironside
The Jeffersons
Laverne & Shirley
*M*A*S*H*
Marcus Welby, M.D.
Maude
Mork & Mindy
Phyllis
Rhoda
Sanford and Son
That's Incredible
Three's Company
The Waltons

Television

1970   Drama: *The Senator,* The Bold Ones (NBC)

Comedy: *All in the Family* (CBS)

Actor Drama: **Hal Holbrook,** *The Senator, The Bold Ones* (NBC)

Actress Drama: **Susan Hampshire,** *The First Churchills, Masterpiece Theatre* (PBS)

Actor Comedy: **Jack Klugman,** *The Odd Couple* (ABC)

Actress Comedy: **Jean Stapleton,** *All in the Family* (CBS)

1971   Drama: *Elizabeth R, Masterpiece Theatre* (PBS)

Comedy: *All in the Family* (CBS)

Actor Drama: **Peter Falk,** *Columbo, NBC Mystery Movie* (NBC)

Actress Drama: **Glenda Jackson,** *Elizabeth R, Masterpiece Theatre* (PBS)

Actor Comedy: **Carroll O'Connor,** *All in the Family* (CBS)

Actress Comedy: **Jean Stapleton,** *All in the Family* (CBS)

1972   Drama: *The Waltons* (CBS)

Comedy: *All in the Family* (CBS)

Actor Drama: **Richard Thomas,** *The Waltons* (CBS)

Actress Drama: **Michael Learned,** *The Waltons* (CBS)

Actor Comedy: **Jack Klugman,** *The Odd Couple* (ABC)

Actress Comedy: **Mary Tyler Moore,** *The Mary Tyler Moore Show* (CBS)

1973   Drama: *Upstairs, Downstairs, Masterpiece Theatre* (PBS)

Comedy: *M*A*S*H* (CBS)

Actor Drama: **Telly Savalas,** *Kojak* (CBS)

Actress Drama: **Michael Learned,** *The Waltons* (CBS)

Actor Comedy: **Alan Alda,** *M*A*S*H* (CBS)

Actress Comedy: **Mary Tyler Moore,** *The Mary Tyler Moore Show* (CBS)

1974   Drama: *Upstairs, Downstairs, Masterpiece Theatre* (PBS)

Comedy: *The Mary Tyler Moore Show* (CBS)

Actor Drama: **Robert Blake,** *Baretta* (ABC)

Actress Drama: **Jean Marsh,** *Upstairs, Downstairs, Masterpiece Theatre* (PBS)

Actor Comedy: **Tony Randall,** *The Odd Couple* (ABC)

Actress Comedy: **Valerie Harper,** *Rhoda* (CBS)

Television

1975   Drama: *Police Story* (NBC)
Comedy: *The Mary Tyler Moore Show* (CBS)
Actor Drama: **Peter Falk,** *Columbo* (NBC)
Actress Drama: **Michael Learned,** *The Waltons* (CBS)
Actor Comedy: **Jack Albertson,** *Chico and the Man* (NBC)
Actress Comedy: **Mary Tyler Moore,** *The Mary Tyler Moore Show* (CBS)

1976   Drama: *Upstairs, Downstairs, Masterpiece Theatre* (PBS)
Comedy: *The Mary Tyler Moore Show* (CBS)
Actor Drama: **James Garner,** *The Rockford Files* (NBC)
Actress Drama: **Lindsay Wagner,** *The Bionic Woman* (ABC)
Actor Comedy: **Carroll O'Connor,** *All in the Family* (CBS)
Actress Comedy: **Beatrice Arthur,** *Maude* (CBS)

1977   Drama: *The Rockford Files* (NBC)
Comedy: *All in the Family* (CBS)
Actor Drama: **Ed Asner,** *Lou Grant* (CBS)
Actress Drama: **Sada Thompson,** *Family* (ABC)
Actor Comedy: **Carroll O'Connor,** *All in the Family* (CBS)
Actress Comedy: **Jean Stapleton,** *All in the Family* (CBS)

1978   Drama: *Lou Grant* (CBS)
Comedy: *Taxi* (ABC)
Actor Drama: **Ron Leibman,** *Kaz* (CBS)
Actress Drama: **Mariette Hartley,** *The Incredible Hulk* (CBS)
Actor Comedy: **Carroll O'Connor,** *All in the Family* (CBS)
Actress Comedy: **Ruth Gordon,** *Taxi* (ABC)

1979   Drama: *Lou Grant* (CBS)
Comedy: *Taxi* (ABC)
Actor Drama: **Ed Asner,** *Lou Grant* (CBS)
Actress Drama: **Barbara Bel Geddes,** *Dallas* (CBS)
Actor Comedy: **Richard Mulligan,** *Soap* (ABC)
Actress Comedy: **Cathryn Damon,** *Soap* (ABC)

the **70s**

Music

Night Fever The Bee Gees

You Light Up My Life Debbie Boone

Le Freak Chic

Shadow Dancing Andy Gibb

My Sharona The Knack

Joy to the World Three Dog Night

Tonight's the Night (Gonna Be Alright) Rod Stewart

Do Ya Think I'm Sexy? Rod Stewart

How Deep is Your Love The Bee Gees

Stayin' Alive The Bee Gees

Reunited Peaches & Herb

Hot Stuff Donna Summer

Three Times A Lady The Commodores

Afternoon Delight Starlight Vocal Band

American Pie Don McLean

The First Time Ever I Saw Your Face Roberta Flack

My Love Paul McCartney & Wings

It's Too Late Carole King

One Bad Apple The Osmonds

Bridge Over Troubled Water Simon & Garfunkle

Family Affair Sly & the Family Stone

My Sweet Lord George Harrison

Let It Be The Beatles

Hot Child in the City Nick Gilder

I Just Want to Be Your Everything Andy Gibb

Love Theme From 'A Star is Born' (Evergreen) Barbra Streisand

Best of My Love The Emotions

Boogie Oogie Oogie A Taste of Honey

Tie A Yellow Ribbon Round the Old Oak Tree Tony Orlando & Dawn

Torn Between Two Lovers Mary MacGregor

Music

Academy Award Winner: Best Song

	SONG TITLE	MOVIE
1970	*For All We Know*	*Lovers and Other Strangers*
1971	*Theme from Shaft*	*Shaft*
1972	*The Morning After*	*The Poseidon Adventure*
1973	*The Way We Were*	*The Way We Were*
1974	*We May Never Love Like This Again*	*The Towering Inferno*
1975	*I'm Easy*	*Nashville*
1976	*Evergreen*	*A Star Is Born*
1977	*You Light Up My Life*	*You Light Up My Life*
1978	*Last Dance*	*Thank God It's Friday*
1979	*It Goes Like It Goes*	*Norma Rae*

Grammy Award: Record of the Year

	SONG TITLE	MOVIE
1970	*Bridge Over Troubled Water*	*Simon & Garfunkel*
1971	*It's Too Late*	*Carole King*
1972	*The First Time Ever I Saw Your Face*	*Roberta Flack*
1973	*Killing Me Softly With His Song*	*Roberta Flack*
1974	*I Honestly Love You*	*Olivia Newton-John*
1975	*Love Will Keep Us Together*	*The Captain & Tennille*
1976	*This Masquerade*	*George Benson*
1977	*Hotel California*	*Eagles*
1978	*Just The Way You Are*	*Billy Joel*
1979	*What A Fool Believes*	*Doobie Brothers*

Fashion

Founded in 1942 by Coty, the perfume and cosmetics company, these awards were one of the first in fashion and arguably the most prestigious. Fashion journalists, under Coty's sponsorship, chose the winners. Categories included women's wear (Winnie); men's wear, begun in 1968 (no name); and repeat winners (Return or Hall of Fame). The Coty awards were discontinued in 1985.

1970
Winnies: **Giorgio di Sant Angelo, Chester Weinberg**
Men's Wear: **Ralph Lauren**
Return Award: **Herbert Kasper**
Hall of Fame: **Bill Blass**

1971
Winnies: **Halston, Betsy Johnson**
Men's Wear: **Larry Kane**
Hall of Fame: **Anne Klein, Bill Blass**

1972
Winnie: **John Anthony**
Return Award: **Halston**
Hall of Fame: **Bonnie Cashin**

1973
Winnies: **Stephen Burrows, Calvin Klein**
Men's Wear: **Piero Dimitri**
Return Award: **Ralph Lauren**
Hall of Fame: **Oscar de la Renta**

1974
Winnie: **Ralph Lauren**
Men's Wear: **Bill Kaiserman**
Return Awards: **Calvin Klein, Piero Dimitri**
Hall of Fame: **Geoffrey Beene, Halston**

Fashion

Coty American Fashion Critics Awards 1975-1979

1975   Winnie: **Carol Horn**
Men's Wear: **Chuck Howard and Peter Wrigley**
Hall of Fame: **Geoffrey Beene, Piero Dimitri, Calvin Klein**

1976   Winnie: **Mary McFadden**
Return Awards: **John Anthony, Ralph Lauren**
Hall of Fame: **Herbert Kasper, Bill Kaiserman**

1977   Winnies: **Stephen Burrows, Louis Dell'Olio, Donna Karan**
Men's Wear: **Alexander Julian**
Hall of Fame: **Ralph Lauren**
Return Award: **John Anthony**

1978   Men's Wear: **Robert Stock**
Return Award: **Mary McFadden**

1979   Winnie: **Perry Ellis**
Men's Wear: **Lee Wright**
Hall of Fame: **Mary McFadden**
Return Award: **Alexander Julian**

The Neiman Marcus Awards

Founded by the famous department store in 1938, these awards are not limited to fashion designers but also given to couturiers, fashionable figures and show biz personalities. They are given out sporadically.

1973   **Ralph Lauren, Mr. And Mrs. Ottavio Missoni, Hanae Mori, Jean Muir, Levi Strauss and Company**

1979   **Giorgio Armani, Richard Avedon, the Artisans of Baccarat, Perry Ellis, Mary McFadden**

2007

january
S	M	T	W	T	F	S
	1	2	3	4	5	6
7	8	9	10	11	12	13
14	15	16	17	18	19	20
21	22	23	24	25	26	27
28	29	30	31			

february
S	M	T	W	T	F	S
				1	2	3
4	5	6	7	8	9	10
11	12	13	14	15	16	17
18	19	20	21	22	23	24
25	26	27	28			

march
S	M	T	W	T	F	S
				1	2	3
4	5	6	7	8	9	10
11	12	13	14	15	16	17
18	19	20	21	22	23	24
25	26	27	28	29	30	31

april
S	M	T	W	T	F	S
1	2	3	4	5	6	7
8	9	10	11	12	13	14
15	16	17	18	19	20	21
22	23	24	25	26	27	28
29	30					

may
S	M	T	W	T	F	S
		1	2	3	4	5
6	7	8	9	10	11	12
13	14	15	16	17	18	19
20	21	22	23	24	25	26
27	28	29	30	31		

june
S	M	T	W	T	F	S
					1	2
3	4	5	6	7	8	9
10	11	12	13	14	15	16
17	18	19	20	21	22	23
24	25	26	27	28	29	30

july
S	M	T	W	T	F	S
1	2	3	4	5	6	7
8	9	10	11	12	13	14
15	16	17	18	19	20	21
22	23	24	25	26	27	28
29	30	31				

august
S	M	T	W	T	F	S
			1	2	3	4
5	6	7	8	9	10	11
12	13	14	15	16	17	18
19	20	21	22	23	24	25
26	27	28	29	30	31	

september
S	M	T	W	T	F	S
						1
2	3	4	5	6	7	8
9	10	11	12	13	14	15
16	17	18	19	20	21	22
$^{23}/_{30}$	24	25	26	27	28	29

october
S	M	T	W	T	F	S
	1	2	3	4	5	6
7	8	9	10	11	12	13
14	15	16	17	18	19	20
21	22	23	24	25	26	27
28	29	30	31			

november
S	M	T	W	T	F	S
				1	2	3
4	5	6	7	8	9	10
11	12	13	14	15	16	17
18	19	20	21	22	23	24
25	26	27	28	29	30	

december
S	M	T	W	T	F	S
						1
2	3	4	5	6	7	8
9	10	11	12	13	14	15
16	17	18	19	20	21	22
$^{23}/_{30}$	$^{24}/_{31}$	25	26	27	28	29

2008

january
S	M	T	W	T	F	S
		1	2	3	4	5
6	7	8	9	10	11	12
13	14	15	16	17	18	19
20	21	22	23	24	25	26
27	28	29	30	31		

february
S	M	T	W	T	F	S
					1	2
3	4	5	6	7	8	9
10	11	12	13	14	15	16
17	18	19	20	21	22	23
24	25	26	27	28	29	

march
S	M	T	W	T	F	S
						1
2	3	4	5	6	7	8
9	10	11	12	13	14	15
16	17	18	19	20	21	22
$^{23}/_{30}$	$^{24}/_{31}$	25	26	27	28	29

april
S	M	T	W	T	F	S
		1	2	3	4	5
6	7	8	9	10	11	12
13	14	15	16	17	18	19
20	21	22	23	24	25	26
27	28	29	30			

may
S	M	T	W	T	F	S
				1	2	3
4	5	6	7	8	9	10
11	12	13	14	15	16	17
18	19	20	21	22	23	24
25	26	27	28	29	30	

june
S	M	T	W	T	F	S
1	2	3	4	5	6	7
8	9	10	11	12	13	14
15	16	17	18	19	20	21
22	23	24	25	26	27	28
29	30					

july
S	M	T	W	T	F	S
		1	2	3	4	5
6	7	8	9	10	11	12
13	14	15	16	17	18	19
20	21	22	23	24	25	26
27	28	29	30	31		

august
S	M	T	W	T	F	S
					1	2
3	4	5	6	7	8	9
10	11	12	13	14	15	16
17	18	19	20	21	22	23
$^{24}/_{31}$	25	26	27	28	29	30

september
S	M	T	W	T	F	S
	1	2	3	4	5	6
7	8	9	10	11	12	13
14	15	16	17	18	19	20
21	22	23	24	25	26	27
28	29	30				

october
S	M	T	W	T	F	S
			1	2	3	4
5	6	7	8	9	10	11
12	13	14	15	16	17	18
19	20	21	22	23	24	25
26	27	28	29	30	31	

november
S	M	T	W	T	F	S
						1
2	3	4	5	6	7	8
9	10	11	12	13	14	15
16	17	18	19	20	21	22
$^{23}/_{30}$	24	25	26	27	28	29

december
S	M	T	W	T	F	S
	1	2	3	4	5	6
7	8	9	10	11	12	13
14	15	16	17	18	19	20
21	22	23	24	25	26	27
28	29	30	31			

Addresses

Addresses

Addresses

NAME	HOME
ADDRESS	WORK
E-MAIL	CELL

NAME	HOME
ADDRESS	WORK
E-MAIL	CELL

NAME	HOME
ADDRESS	WORK
E-MAIL	CELL

NAME	HOME
ADDRESS	WORK
E-MAIL	CELL

NAME	HOME
ADDRESS	WORK
E-MAIL	CELL

NAME	HOME
ADDRESS	WORK
E-MAIL	CELL

NAME	HOME
ADDRESS	WORK
E-MAIL	CELL

NAME	HOME
ADDRESS	WORK
E-MAIL	CELL

NAME	HOME
ADDRESS	WORK
E-MAIL	CELL

NAME	HOME
ADDRESS	WORK
E-MAIL	CELL

NAME	HOME
ADDRESS	WORK
E-MAIL	CELL

NAME	HOME
ADDRESS	WORK
E-MAIL	CELL

NAME	HOME
ADDRESS	WORK
E-MAIL	CELL

NAME	HOME
ADDRESS	WORK
E-MAIL	CELL

NAME	HOME
ADDRESS	WORK
E-MAIL	CELL

NAME	HOME
ADDRESS	WORK
E-MAIL	CELL

NAME	HOME
ADDRESS	WORK
E-MAIL	CELL

NAME	HOME
ADDRESS	WORK
E-MAIL	CELL

NAME	HOME
ADDRESS	WORK
E-MAIL	CELL

NAME	HOME
ADDRESS	WORK
E-MAIL	CELL

NAME	HOME
ADDRESS	WORK
E-MAIL	CELL

NAME	HOME
ADDRESS	WORK
E-MAIL	CELL

NAME	HOME
ADDRESS	WORK
E-MAIL	CELL

NAME	HOME
ADDRESS	WORK
E-MAIL	CELL

NAME	HOME
ADDRESS	WORK
E-MAIL	CELL

Addresses

NAME	HOME
ADDRESS	WORK
E-MAIL	CELL
NAME	HOME
ADDRESS	WORK
E-MAIL	CELL
NAME	HOME
ADDRESS	WORK
E-MAIL	CELL
NAME	HOME
ADDRESS	WORK
E-MAIL	CELL
NAME	HOME
ADDRESS	WORK
E-MAIL	CELL
NAME	HOME
ADDRESS	WORK
E-MAIL	CELL
NAME	HOME
ADDRESS	WORK
E-MAIL	CELL
NAME	HOME
ADDRESS	WORK
E-MAIL	CELL
NAME	HOME
ADDRESS	WORK
E-MAIL	CELL
NAME	HOME
ADDRESS	WORK
E-MAIL	CELL
NAME	HOME
ADDRESS	WORK
E-MAIL	CELL
NAME	HOME
ADDRESS	WORK
E-MAIL	CELL

NAME

ADDRESS

E-MAIL

HOME

WORK

CELL

NAME

ADDRESS

E-MAIL

HOME

WORK

CELL

NAME

ADDRESS

E-MAIL

HOME

WORK

CELL

NAME

ADDRESS

E-MAIL

HOME

WORK

CELL

NAME

ADDRESS

E-MAIL

HOME

WORK

CELL

NAME

ADDRESS

E-MAIL

HOME

WORK

CELL

NAME

ADDRESS

E-MAIL

HOME

WORK

CELL

NAME

ADDRESS

E-MAIL

HOME

WORK

CELL

NAME

ADDRESS

E-MAIL

HOME

WORK

CELL

NAME

ADDRESS

E-MAIL

HOME

WORK

CELL

NAME

ADDRESS

E-MAIL

HOME

WORK

CELL

NAME

ADDRESS

E-MAIL

HOME

WORK

CELL

Addresses

NAME	HOME
ADDRESS	WORK
E-MAIL	CELL

NAME	HOME
ADDRESS	WORK
E-MAIL	CELL

NAME	HOME
ADDRESS	WORK
E-MAIL	CELL

NAME	HOME
ADDRESS	WORK
E-MAIL	CELL

NAME	HOME
ADDRESS	WORK
E-MAIL	CELL

NAME	HOME
ADDRESS	WORK
E-MAIL	CELL

NAME	HOME
ADDRESS	WORK
E-MAIL	CELL

NAME	HOME
ADDRESS	WORK
E-MAIL	CELL

NAME	HOME
ADDRESS	WORK
E-MAIL	CELL

NAME	HOME
ADDRESS	WORK
E-MAIL	CELL

NAME	HOME
ADDRESS	WORK
E-MAIL	CELL

NAME	HOME
ADDRESS	WORK
E-MAIL	CELL

NAME	HOME
ADDRESS	WORK
E-MAIL	CELL

NAME	HOME
ADDRESS	WORK
E-MAIL	CELL

NAME	HOME
ADDRESS	WORK
E-MAIL	CELL

NAME	HOME
ADDRESS	WORK
E-MAIL	CELL

NAME	HOME
ADDRESS	WORK
E-MAIL	CELL

NAME	HOME
ADDRESS	WORK
E-MAIL	CELL

NAME	HOME
ADDRESS	WORK
E-MAIL	CELL

NAME	HOME
ADDRESS	WORK
E-MAIL	CELL

NAME	HOME
ADDRESS	WORK
E-MAIL	CELL

NAME	HOME
ADDRESS	WORK
E-MAIL	CELL

NAME	HOME
ADDRESS	WORK
E-MAIL	CELL

NAME	HOME
ADDRESS	WORK
E-MAIL	CELL

NAME	HOME
ADDRESS	WORK
E-MAIL	CELL

Addresses

NAME	HOME
ADDRESS	WORK
E-MAIL	CELL

NAME	HOME
ADDRESS	WORK
E-MAIL	CELL

NAME	HOME
ADDRESS	WORK
E-MAIL	CELL

NAME	HOME
ADDRESS	WORK
E-MAIL	CELL

NAME	HOME
ADDRESS	WORK
E-MAIL	CELL

NAME	HOME
ADDRESS	WORK
E-MAIL	CELL

NAME	HOME
ADDRESS	WORK
E-MAIL	CELL

NAME	HOME
ADDRESS	WORK
E-MAIL	CELL

NAME	HOME
ADDRESS	WORK
E-MAIL	CELL

NAME	HOME
ADDRESS	WORK
E-MAIL	CELL

NAME	HOME
ADDRESS	WORK
E-MAIL	CELL

NAME	HOME
ADDRESS	WORK
E-MAIL	CELL

NAME	HOME
ADDRESS	WORK
E-MAIL	CELL

T•U

Addresses

NAME		HOME
ADDRESS		WORK
	E-MAIL	CELL
NAME		HOME
ADDRESS		WORK
	E-MAIL	CELL
NAME		HOME
ADDRESS		WORK
	E-MAIL	CELL
NAME		HOME
ADDRESS		WORK
	E-MAIL	CELL
NAME		HOME
ADDRESS		WORK
	E-MAIL	CELL
NAME		HOME
ADDRESS		WORK
	E-MAIL	CELL
NAME		HOME
ADDRESS		WORK
	E-MAIL	CELL
NAME		HOME
ADDRESS		WORK
	E-MAIL	CELL
NAME		HOME
ADDRESS		WORK
	E-MAIL	CELL
NAME		HOME
ADDRESS		WORK
	E-MAIL	CELL
NAME		HOME
ADDRESS		WORK
	E-MAIL	CELL
NAME		HOME
ADDRESS		WORK
	E-MAIL	CELL

Addresses

NAME		HOME
ADDRESS		WORK
	E-MAIL	CELL

NAME		HOME
ADDRESS		WORK
	E-MAIL	CELL

NAME		HOME
ADDRESS		WORK
	E-MAIL	CELL

NAME		HOME
ADDRESS		WORK
	E-MAIL	CELL

NAME		HOME
ADDRESS		WORK
	E-MAIL	CELL

NAME		HOME
ADDRESS		WORK
	E-MAIL	CELL

NAME		HOME
ADDRESS		WORK
	E-MAIL	CELL

NAME		HOME
ADDRESS		WORK
	E-MAIL	CELL

NAME		HOME
ADDRESS		WORK
	E-MAIL	CELL

NAME		HOME
ADDRESS		WORK
	E-MAIL	CELL

NAME		HOME
ADDRESS		WORK
	E-MAIL	CELL

NAME		HOME
ADDRESS		WORK
	E-MAIL	CELL

NAME		HOME	
ADDRESS		WORK	
	E-MAIL	CELL	

NAME		HOME	
ADDRESS		WORK	
	E-MAIL	CELL	

NAME		HOME	
ADDRESS		WORK	
	E-MAIL	CELL	

NAME		HOME	
ADDRESS		WORK	
	E-MAIL	CELL	

NAME		HOME	
ADDRESS		WORK	
	E-MAIL	CELL	

NAME		HOME	
ADDRESS		WORK	
	E-MAIL	CELL	

NAME		HOME	
ADDRESS		WORK	
	E-MAIL	CELL	

NAME		HOME	
ADDRESS		WORK	
	E-MAIL	CELL	

NAME		HOME	
ADDRESS		WORK	
	E-MAIL	CELL	

NAME		HOME	
ADDRESS		WORK	
	E-MAIL	CELL	

NAME		HOME	
ADDRESS		WORK	
	E-MAIL	CELL	

NAME		HOME	
ADDRESS		WORK	
	E-MAIL	CELL	

Milestones

Birthstones

MONTH	STONE	MEANING
January	**Garnet**	loyalty and strength
February	**Amethyst**	sincerity and wealth
March	**Aquamarine**	health and hope
April	**Diamond**	brilliance and love
May	**Emerald**	peace and hope
June	**Pearl**	wisdom and faithfulness
July	**Ruby**	happiness and beauty
August	**Peridot**	happiness and friendship
September	**Sapphire**	truth and calmness
October	**Opal**	hope and confidence
November	**Topaz**	goodness and friendship
December	**Turquoise**	good health

Birth Flowers

MONTH	FLOWER	MEANING
January	**Snowdrop**	good health
February	**Primrose**	peace of mind
March	**Daffodil**	loyalty
April	**Sweet Pea**	good fortune
May	**Hawthorne**	courage
June	**Rose**	love
July	**Water Lily**	success
August	**Poppy**	fame
September	**Morning Glory**	affection
October	**Cosmos**	friendship
November	**Chrysanthemum**	cheerfulness
December	**Holly**	courage

Anniversary Gifts

YEAR	TRADITIONAL	MODERN
1	**Paper**	Clocks
2	**Cotton**	China
3	**Leather**	Crystal/Glass
4	**Fruit/Flowers**	Appliances
5	**Wood**	Silverware
6	**Candy/Iron**	Wood
7	**Copper/Wool**	Desk Sets
8	**Bronze/Pottery**	Linens/Lace
9	**Pottery/Willow**	Leather
10	**Tin, Aluminum**	Diamond Jewelry
11	**Steel**	Fashion Jewelry
12	**Silk/Linen**	Pearl
13	**Lace**	Textiles/Furs
14	**Ivory**	Gold Jewelry
15	**Crystal**	Watches
20	**China**	Platinum
25	**Silver**	Silver
30	**Pearl**	Diamond
35	**Coral**	Jade
40	**Ruby**	Ruby
45	**Sapphire**	Sapphire
50	**Gold**	Gold
55	**Emerald**	Emerald
60	**Diamond**	Diamond

Many organizations present different interpretations of birthstones, birth flowers and anniversary gifts. These are our best approximation.

Size Conversions

American, British and European Size Conversion Tables

WOMEN

Dresses, Suits and Coats

American	8	10	12	14	16	18	
British	30	32	34	36	38	40	
European	36	38	40	42	44	46	

Blouses and Sweaters

American	32	34	36	38	40	42	
British	34	36	38	40	42	44	
European	40	42	44	46	48	50	

Shoes

American	6	6-1/2	7	7-1/2	8	8-1/2	9
British	4-1/2	5	5-1/2	6	6-1/2	7	7-1/2
European	36	37	38	38	38-1/2	39	40

MEN

Suits and Overcoats

American & British	36	38	40	42	44	46	48
European	46	48	50	52	54	56	58

Shirts

American & British	14	14-1/2	15	15-1/2	16	16-1/2	17
European	36	37	38	39	40	41	42

Shoes

American	8	8-1/2	9	9-1/2	10	10-1/2
British	7-1/2	8	8-1/2	9	9-1/2	10
European	40	41	42	43	44	45

CHILDREN

American	4	6	8	10	12
British (ins)	43	48	55	58	60
European (cm)	125	135	150	155	160

Size conversion tables vary, as do actual garments. These are approximate calculations.